Pearson
Edexcel Level 1/Level 2
GCSE (9–1) in Mathematics (1MA1)

Sample Assessment Materials

First teaching from September 2015
First certification from June 2017

Issue 2

PEARSON

Edexcel, BTEC and LCCI qualifications

Edexcel, BTEC and LCCI qualifications are awarded by Pearson, the UK's largest awarding body offering academic and vocational qualifications that are globally recognised and benchmarked. For further information, please visit our qualification websites at www.edexcel.com, www.btec.co.uk or www.lcci.org.uk. Alternatively, you can get in touch with us using the details on our contact us page at qualifications.pearson.com/contactus

About Pearson

Pearson is the world's leading learning company, with 40,000 employees in more than 70 countries working to help people of all ages to make measurable progress in their lives through learning. We put the learner at the centre of everything we do, because wherever learning flourishes, so do people. Find out more about how we can help you and your learners at qualifications.pearson.com

References to third party material made in this document are made in good faith. Pearson does not endorse, approve or accept responsibility for the content of materials, which may be subject to change, or any opinions expressed therein. (Material may include textbooks, journals, magazines and other publications and websites.)

All information in this document is correct at time of publication.

Original origami artwork: Mark Bolitho
Origami photography: Pearson Education Ltd/Naki Kouyioumtzis

ISBN 9781446927212

All the material in this publication is copyright
© Pearson Education Limited 2015

Contents

Introduction

The Pearson Edexcel Level 1/Level 2 GCSE (9-1) in Mathematics is designed for use in schools and colleges. It is part of a suite of GCSE qualifications offered by Pearson.

These sample assessment materials have been developed to support this qualification and will be used as the benchmark to develop the assessment students will take.

© Pearson Education Limited 2015

General marking guidance

These notes offer general guidance, but the specific notes for examiners appertaining to individual questions take precedence.

1 All candidates must receive the same treatment. Examiners must mark the last candidate in exactly the same way as they mark the first.

Where some judgement is required, mark schemes will provide the principles by which marks will be awarded; exemplification/indicative content will not be exhaustive.

2 All the marks on the mark scheme are designed to be awarded; mark schemes should be applied positively. Examiners should also be prepared to award zero marks if the candidate's response is not worthy of credit according to the mark scheme. If there is a wrong answer (or no answer) indicated on the answer line always check the working in the body of the script (and on any diagrams), and award any marks appropriate from the mark scheme.

Questions where working is not required: In general, the correct answer should be given full marks.

Questions that specifically require working: In general, candidates who do not show working on this type of question will get no marks – full details will be given in the mark scheme for each individual question.

3 **Crossed out work**

This should be marked **unless** the candidate has replaced it with an alternative response.

4 **Choice of method**

If there is a choice of methods shown, mark the method that leads to the answer given on the answer line.

If no answer appears on the answer line, mark both methods **then award the lower number of marks.**

5 **Incorrect method**

If it is clear from the working that the "correct" answer has been obtained from incorrect working, award 0 marks. Send the response to review for your Team Leader to check.

6 **Follow through marks**

Follow through marks which involve a single stage calculation can be awarded without working as you can check the answer, but if ambiguous do not award.

Follow through marks which involve more than one stage of calculation can only be awarded on sight of the relevant working, even if it appears obvious that there is only one way you could get the answer given.

© Pearson Education Limited 2015

7 Ignoring subsequent work

It is appropriate to ignore subsequent work when the additional work does not change the answer in a way that is inappropriate for the question or its context. (eg. an incorrectly cancelled fraction when the unsimplified fraction would gain full marks).

It is not appropriate to ignore subsequent work when the additional work essentially makes the answer incorrect (eg. incorrect algebraic simplification).

8 Probability

Probability answers must be given as a fraction, percentage or decimal. If a candidate gives a decimal equivalent to a probability, this should be written to at least 2 decimal places (unless tenths).

Incorrect notation should lose the accuracy marks, but be awarded any implied method marks.

If a probability answer is given on the answer line using both incorrect and correct notation, award the marks.

If a probability fraction is given then cancelled incorrectly, ignore the incorrectly cancelled answer.

9 Linear equations

Unless indicated otherwise in the mark scheme, full marks can be gained if the solution alone is given on the answer line, or otherwise unambiguously identified in working (without contradiction elsewhere). Where the correct solution only is shown substituted, but not identified as the solution, the accuracy mark is lost but any method marks can be awarded (embedded answers).

10 Range of answers

Unless otherwise stated, when an answer is given as a range (e.g 3.5 – 4.2) then this is inclusive of the end points (e.g 3.5, 4.2) and all numbers within the range.

Guidance on the use of abbreviations within this mark scheme	
M	method mark awarded for a correct method or partial method
P	process mark awarded for a correct process as part of a problem solving question
A	accuracy mark (awarded after a correct method or process; if no method or process is seen then full marks for the question are implied but see individual mark schemes for more details)
C	communication mark
B	unconditional accuracy mark (no method needed)
oe	or equivalent
cao	correct answer only
ft	follow through (when appropriate as per mark scheme)
sc	special case
dep	dependent (on a previous mark)
indep	independent
awrt	answer which rounds to
isw	ignore subsequent working

Pearson Edexcel Level 1/Level 2 GCSE (9-1) in Mathematics - Sample Assessment Materials (SAMs) - Issue 2 - June 2015
© Pearson Education Limited 2015

Write your name here

Surname		Other names

Pearson Edexcel
Level 1/Level 2 GCSE (9 - 1)

Centre Number

Candidate Number

Mathematics
Paper 1 (Non-Calculator)

Foundation Tier

Sample Assessment Materials – Issue 2
Time: 1 hour 30 minutes

Paper Reference
1MA1/1F

You must have: Ruler graduated in centimetres and millimetres, protractor, pair of compasses, pen, HB pencil, eraser.

Total Marks

Instructions

- Use **black** ink or ball-point pen.
- **Fill in the boxes** at the top of this page with your name, centre number and candidate number.
- Answer **all** questions.
- Answer the questions in the spaces provided
  – *there may be more space than you need.*
- **Calculators may not be used.**
- Diagrams are **NOT** accurately drawn, unless otherwise indicated.
- You must **show all your working out**.

Information

- The total mark for this paper is 80
- The marks for **each** question are shown in brackets
  – *use this as a guide as to how much time to spend on each question.*

Advice

- Read each question carefully before you start to answer it.
- Keep an eye on the time.
- Try to answer every question.
- Check your answers if you have time at the end.

Turn over ▶

S48571A
©2015 Pearson Education Ltd.
6/4/7/7/7/4/6/6/6/6/

Answer ALL questions.

Write your answers in the spaces provided.

You must write down all the stages in your working.

1   Write the following numbers in order of size.
    Start with the smallest number.

$$0.61 \qquad 0.1 \qquad 0.16 \qquad 0.106$$

....

(Total for Question 1 is 1 mark)

2   Write 0.037 as a fraction.

....

(Total for Question 2 is 1 mark)

3   Write down the 20th odd number.

....

(Total for Question 3 is 1 mark)

Pearson Edexcel Level I/Level 2 GCSE (9-1) in Mathematics - Sample Assessment Materials (SAMs) - Issue 2 - June 2015
© Pearson Education Limited 2015

4 Write down all the factors of 20

....

(Total for Question 4 is 2 marks)

5 Tanya needs to buy chocolate bars for all the children in Year 7
Each of the 130 children get one chocolate bar.

There are 8 chocolate bars in each packet.

Work out the least number of packets of chocolate bars that Tanya needs to buy.

....

(Total for Question 5 is 3 marks)

6 Greg rolls a fair ordinary dice once.

(i) On the probability scale, mark with a cross (×) the probability that the dice will land on an odd number.

$$0 \qquad \frac{1}{2} \qquad 1$$

(ii) On the probability scale, mark with a cross (×) the probability that the dice will land on a number less than 5

$$0 \qquad \frac{1}{2} \qquad 1$$

(Total for Question 6 is 2 marks)

7 One day Sally earned £60
She worked for 8 hours.

Work out Sally's hourly rate of pay.

£...................................

(Total for Question 7 is 2 marks)

8 Work out 15% of 80

....

(Total for Question 8 is 2 marks)

9 There are 3 red beads and 1 blue bead in a jar.
A bead is taken at random from the jar.

What is the probability that the bead is blue?

....

(Total for Question 9 is 1 mark)

10 There are only black pens and green pens in a box.
The ratio of the number of black pens in the box to the number of green pens in the box
is 2 : 5

What fraction of the pens are black?

....

(Total for Question 10 is 1 mark)

11 Sally has three tiles.
Each tile has a different number on it.
Sally puts the three tiles down to make a number.
Each number is made with all three tiles.

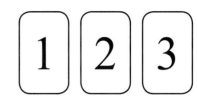

How many different numbers can Sally make?

(Total for Question 11 is 2 marks)

© Pearson Education Limited 2015

12 Here are the first three patterns in a sequence.
   The patterns are made from triangles and rectangles.

pattern number 1   pattern number 2   pattern number 3

(a) How many triangles are there in pattern number 7?

....

(2)

Charlie says

   "There are 4 rectangles in pattern number 3 so there will be 8 rectangles in pattern number 6"

(b) Is Charlie right?
   Give a reason for your answer.

....

....

(1)

(Total for Question 12 is 3 marks)

13 Paul organised an event for a charity.

Each ticket for the event cost £19.95
Paul sold 395 tickets.

Paul paid costs of £6000
He gave all money left to the charity.

(a) Work out an estimate for the amount of money Paul gave to the charity.

£.......................................

(3)

(b) Is your answer to (a) an underestimate or an overestimate?
Give a reason for your answer.

....

....

(1)

(Total for Question 13 is 4 marks)

14 The table shows information about the numbers of fruit trees in an orchard.

Apple tree	Pear tree	Plum tree
45	20	25

(a) The pictogram shows this information.

Complete the key for the pictogram.

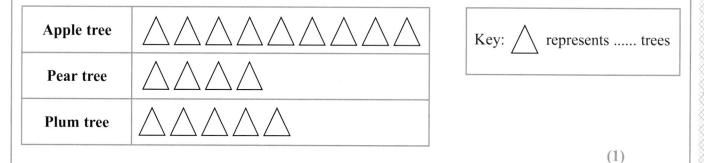

(1)

(b) There are 90 fruit trees in the orchard.

Apple tree	Pear tree	Plum tree
45	20	25

Draw an accurate pie chart for this information.

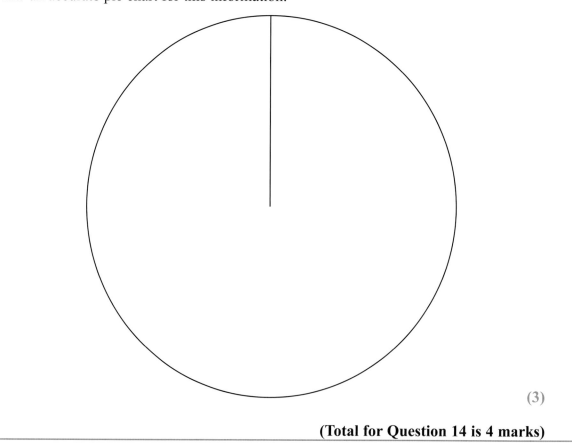

(3)

(Total for Question 14 is 4 marks)

15 Carpet tiles are going to be used to cover a floor.

The floor is a 1200 mm by 1000 mm rectangle.
Each carpet tile is a 40 cm by 30 cm rectangle.

Exactly 10 carpet tiles can be used to cover the floor completely.

Show in a labelled sketch how this can be done.

(Total for Question 15 is 3 marks)

© Pearson Education Limited 2015

16 Sam buys 20 boxes of oranges.
There are 25 oranges in each box.

Each boxes of oranges costs £7

Sam sells $\frac{2}{5}$ of the oranges he bought.

He sells each of these oranges for 40p.

He then sells each of the remaining oranges at 3 oranges for 50p.

Did Sam make a profit or did Sam make a loss?
You must show working to justify your answer.

(Total for Question 16 is 5 marks)

Pearson Edexcel Level 1/Level 2 GCSE (9-1) in Mathematics - Sample Assessment Materials (SAMs) - Issue 2 - June 2015
© Pearson Education Limited 2015

17 100 students had some homework.

42 of these students are boys.
8 of the 100 students did **not** do their homework.
53 of the girls did do their homework.

(a) Use this information to complete the frequency tree.

(3)

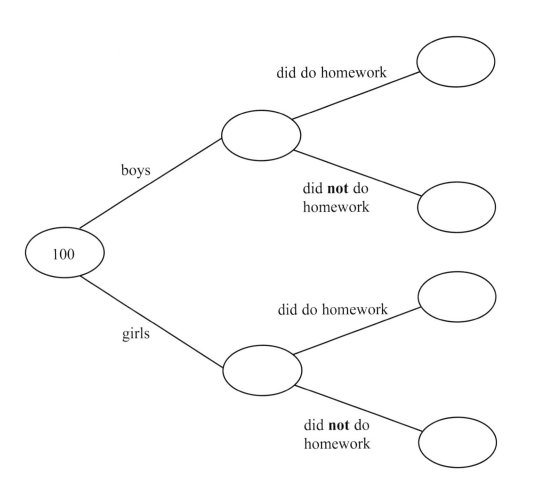

One of the girls is chosen at random.

(b) Work out the probability that this girl did **not** do her homework.

(2)

(Total for Question 17 is 5 marks)

18 (a) Work out $\dfrac{2}{7} + \dfrac{1}{5}$

....

(2)

(b) Work out $1\dfrac{2}{3} \div \dfrac{3}{4}$

....

(2)

(Total for Question 18 is 4 marks)

19 Solve $4x + 5 = x + 26$

$x = $ ....

(Total for Question 19 is 2 marks)

Pearson Edexcel Level 1/Level 2 GCSE (9-1) in Mathematics - Sample Assessment Materials (SAMs) - Issue 2 - June 2015
© Pearson Education Limited 2015

20 In a sale, normal prices are reduced by 20%.
The normal price of a coat is reduced by £15

Work out the normal price of the coat.

£ ....

21 Work out 6.34 × 5.2

....

22 Expand and simplify $(m + 7)(m + 3)$

....

(Total for Question 22 is 2 marks)

23

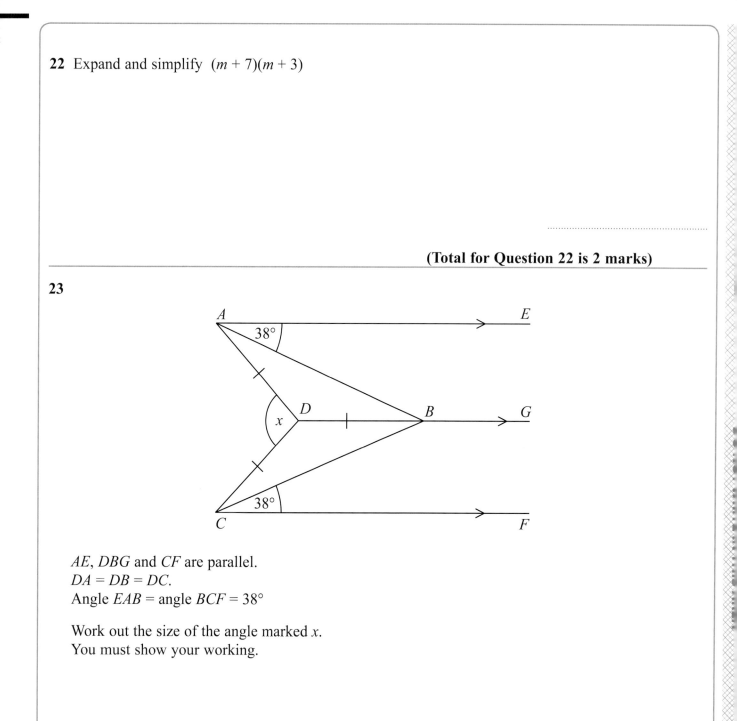

AE, DBG and *CF* are parallel.
DA = DB = DC.
Angle *EAB* = angle *BCF* = 38°

Work out the size of the angle marked *x*.
You must show your working.

....

(Total for Question 23 is 3 marks)

Pearson Edexcel Level 1/Level 2 GCSE (9-1) in Mathematics - Sample Assessment Materials (SAMs) - Issue 2 - June 2015
© Pearson Education Limited 2015

24 Gary drove from London to Sheffield.
It took him 3 hours at an average speed of 80 km/h.

Lyn drove from London to Sheffield.
She took 5 hours.

Assuming that Lyn
      drove along the same roads as Gary
   and did not take a break,

(a) work out Lyn's average speed from London to Sheffield.

....km/h

(3)

(b) If Lyn did **not** drive along the same roads as Gary, explain how this could affect your
answer to part (a).

....

....

(1)

(Total for Question 24 is 4 marks)

25 In a company, the ratio of the number of men to the number of women is $3:2$

40% of the men are under the age of 25
10% of the women are under the age of 25

What percentage of all the people in the company are under the age of 25?

....%

(Total for Question 25 is 4 marks)

26 The plan, front elevation and side elevation of a solid prism are drawn on a centimetre grid.

plan

front elevation   side elevation

In the space below, draw a sketch of the solid prism.
Write the dimensions of the prism on your sketch.

27 There are 1200 students at a school.

Kate is helping to organise a party.
She is going to order pizza.

Kate takes a sample of 60 of the students at the school.
She asks each student to tell her **one** type of pizza they want.

The table shows information about her results.

Pizza	Number of students
ham	20
salami	15
vegetarian	8
margarita	17

Work out how much ham pizza Kate should order.
Write down any assumption you make **and** explain how this could affect your answer.

(Total for Question 27 is 3 marks)

28 Here is a parallelogram.

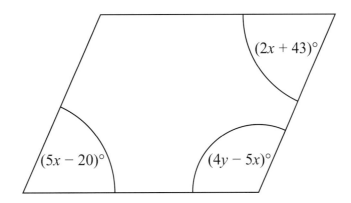

Work out the value of x and the value of y.

$x =$ ....

$y =$ ....

(Total for Question 28 is 5 marks)

29

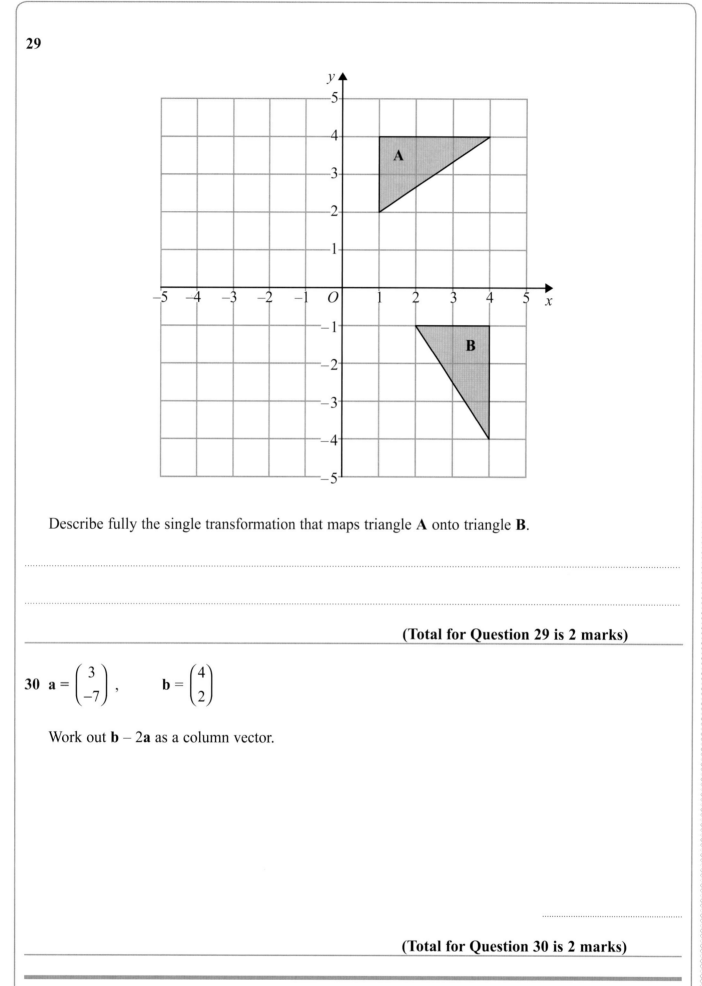

Describe fully the single transformation that maps triangle **A** onto triangle **B**.

....

....

(Total for Question 29 is 2 marks)

30 $\mathbf{a} = \begin{pmatrix} 3 \\ -7 \end{pmatrix}$, $\mathbf{b} = \begin{pmatrix} 4 \\ 2 \end{pmatrix}$

Work out $\mathbf{b} - 2\mathbf{a}$ as a column vector.

....

(Total for Question 30 is 2 marks)

TOTAL FOR PAPER IS 80 MARKS

Pearson Edexcel Level 1/Level 2 GCSE (9-1) in Mathematics - Sample Assessment Materials (SAMs) - Issue 2 - June 2015
© Pearson Education Limited 2015

Question	Working	Answer		Notes
1		0.1, 0.106, 0.16, 0.61	B1	
2		$\dfrac{37}{1000}$	B1	
3		39	B1	
4		1, 2, 4, 5, 10, 20	M1	for at least 3 factors
			A1	for all factors with no additions
5		17	P1	start to process information eg. $130 \div 8$ **or** repeated subtraction from 130 **or** repeated addition
			A1	16.25 **or** 16 remainder 2 **or** 128 **or** 136
			C1	allow ft - interprets answer to round up to integer value
6 (i)		$\times$ at $\dfrac{1}{2}$	B1	
(ii)		$\times$ at $\dfrac{4}{6}$	B1	

© Pearson Education Limited 2015

Question	Working	Answer		Notes
7		7.50	M1	$60 \div 8$
			A1	accept 7.5
8		12	M1	M1 for 0.15×80 oe **or** $8 + 4$
			A1	cao
9		$\dfrac{1}{4}$	B1	$\dfrac{1}{4}$ oe
10		$\dfrac{2}{7}$	B1	
11		6	M1	for starting to list combinations
			A1	cao
12 (a)		18	M1	Evidence of interpretation of pattern, eg. further diagrams drawn or numerical sequence for numbers of triangles 6, 8, 10 etc
			A1	
(b)		No with reason	C1	No with reason eg. No , pattern number 6 will have 7 squares; always one more square than pattern number

Paper 1MA1: 1F

Question		Working	Answer		Notes
13	(a)		2000	P1	Evidence of estimate eg. 400 or 20 used in calculation
				P1	complete process to solve problem
				A1	
	(b)		Overestimate with reason	C1	ft from (a) eg. overestimate as two numbers rounded up
14	(a)		5	B1	
	(b)		Correct pie chart with labels	C1	For apples shown as 'half' ie 180° on pie chart
				C1	All angles calculated correctly (Angles of 180°, 80°, 100°) or pie chart with correct angles
				C1	Fully correct pie chart with labels of apple, pear and plum
15			Correct diagram with layout and lengths	M1	for changing to consistent units eg. $1000 \div 10$ or 40×10
				M1	for interpreting information and a process to fit tiles in floor area eg. may be seen in a sketch or a calculation
				C1	for a diagram to communicate a correct layout with lengths clearly identified
16			loss (supported by correct figures)	P1	process to find total spent eg. 20×7 (=140)
				P1	complete process to find profit from full price oranges eg. $\frac{2}{5} \times 25 \times 20 \times 40 (= 8000)$
				P1	complete process to find profit from reduced price oranges eg. $50 \times \left(\frac{3}{5} \times 25 \times 20 \right) \div 3 (=5000)$
				P1	complete process to find total income with consistent units
				A1	loss with £10 **or** −£10 **or** £130 **and** £140

© Pearson Education Limited 2015

Question	Working	Answer		Notes
17 (a)		42, 58 39, 3, 53, 5	C1	starts to interpret information eg. one correct frequency
			C1	continue to interpret information
			C1	communicates all information correctly
(b)		$\dfrac{5}{58}$	M1	ft for $\dfrac{a}{58}$ with $a < 58$ **or** $\dfrac{5}{b}$ with $b > 5$
			A1	ft from (a)
18 (a)		$\dfrac{17}{35}$	M1	for common denominators with at least one numerator correct
			A1	
(b)		$\dfrac{20}{9}$	M1	for $\dfrac{5}{3} \times \dfrac{4}{3}$ **or** $\dfrac{20}{12} \div \dfrac{9}{12}$
			A1	
19		7	M1	Correct method to isolate terms in x
			A1	
20		75	P1	for start to process eg. linking 20% with 15 or $100 \div 5$ $(=20)$
			A1	

Pearson Edexcel Level 1/Level 2 GCSE (9-1) in Mathematics - Sample Assessment Materials (SAMs) - Issue 2 - June 2015
© Pearson Education Limited 2015

Question	Working	Answer		Notes
21		32.968	M1	for correct method (condone one error)
			A1	for digits 32968
			A1	ft (dep M1) for correct placement of decimal pt
22		$m^2 + 10m + 21$	M1	for at least 3 terms out of a maximum of 4 correct from expansion
			A1	
23		152	M1	Start to method $ABD = 38°$ **and** BAD or DBC or $DCB = 38°$
			M1	ADB or $BDC = 180 - 2 \times 38$ (=104)
			A1	for 152 with working
24 (a)		48	P1	start to process eg. 3×80 (=240)
			P1	'240' $\div$ 5
			A1	
(b)			C1	eg. she may drive a different distance and therefore her average speed could be different

© Pearson Education Limited 2015

Question	Working	Answer		Notes
25		28	P1	Process to start to solve problem eg. $\dfrac{3}{5} \times 40$ **or** divide any number in the ratio 3:2
			P1	Second step in process to solve problem eg. $\dfrac{2}{5} \times 10$ or find number of males/females under 25 for candidate's chosen number
			P1	for complete process
			A1	
26		Correct sketch	C1	interprets diagram eg. draw a solid shape with at least two correct dimensions
			C1	draws correct prism with all necessary dimensions.
27		400	P1	Start to process eg. $1200 \div 60$
			A1	400 oe (accept number of whole pizzas eg. $400 \div 4 = 100$ with 4 people per pizza)
			C1	Eg. Assumption that sample is representative of population – it may not be all 1200 people are going to the party – need less pizza if they don't, assume 4 people per pizza – if different may need more/fewer pizzas

Question	Working	Answer		Notes
28		$x = 21$, $y = 50$	P1	process to start solving problem eg. form an appropriate equation
			P1	complete process to isolate terms in x
			A1	for $x = 21$
			P1	complete process to find second variable
			A1	$y = 50$
29		Rotation of $90°$ clockwise about $(0,0)$	M1	For two of 'rotation' , $(0,0)$, $90°$ clockwise oe
			A1	Correct transformation
30		$\begin{pmatrix} -2 \\ 16 \end{pmatrix}$	C1	For $\begin{pmatrix} 4 \\ 2 \end{pmatrix} - 2 \begin{pmatrix} 3 \\ -7 \end{pmatrix}$
			C1	

Pearson Edexcel Level 1/Level 2 GCSE (9-1) in Mathematics - Sample Assessment Materials (SAMs) - Issue 2 - June 2015
© Pearson Education Limited 2015

Write your name here

Surname

Other names

Pearson Edexcel
Level 1/Level 2 GCSE (9 - 1)

Centre Number

Candidate Number

Mathematics

Paper 2 (Calculator)

Foundation Tier

Sample Assessment Materials – Issue 2
Time: 1 hour 30 minutes

Paper Reference
1MA1/2F

Total Marks

You must have: Ruler graduated in centimetres and millimetres, protractor, pair of compasses, pen, HB pencil, eraser, calculator.

Instructions

- Use **black** ink or ball-point pen.
- **Fill in the boxes** at the top of this page with your name, centre number and candidate number.
- Answer **all** questions.
- Answer the questions in the spaces provided
  – *there may be more space than you need.*
- **Calculators may be used.**
- If your calculator does not have a π button, take the value of π to be 3.142 unless the question instructs otherwise.
- Diagrams are **NOT** accurately drawn, unless otherwise indicated.
- You must **show all your working out.**

Information

- The total mark for this paper is 80
- The marks for **each** question are shown in brackets
  – *use this as a guide as to how much time to spend on each question.*

Advice

- Read each question carefully before you start to answer it.
- Keep an eye on the time.
- Try to answer every question.
- Check your answers if you have time at the end.

Turn over ▶

S48573A
©2015 Pearson Education Ltd.
6/4/7/7/4/6/6/6/

S48573A0120

Answer ALL questions.

Write your answers in the spaces provided.

You must write down all the stages in your working.

1   Write down the value of the 3 in the number 4376

....

(Total for Question 1 is 1 mark)

2   (a) Write $\dfrac{7}{16}$ as a decimal.

....

(Total for Question 2 is 1 mark)

3   Here is a list of numbers

$$4 \quad 7 \quad 9 \quad 25 \quad 27 \quad 31 \quad 64$$

From the numbers in the list, write down a cube number.

....

(Total for Question 3 is 1 mark)

4   Find the value of $(2.8 - 0.45)^2 + \sqrt[3]{5.832}$

....

(Total for Question 4 is 2 marks)

5   There are some boys and girls in a classroom.

The probability of picking at random a boy is $\frac{1}{3}$

What is the probability of picking a girl?

....

6   Jan writes down

one multiple of 9
and two different factors of 40

Jan adds together her three numbers.
Her answer is greater than 20 but less than 30

Find three numbers that Jan could have written down.

....

7 *ABCD* is a square.
This diagram is drawn accurately.

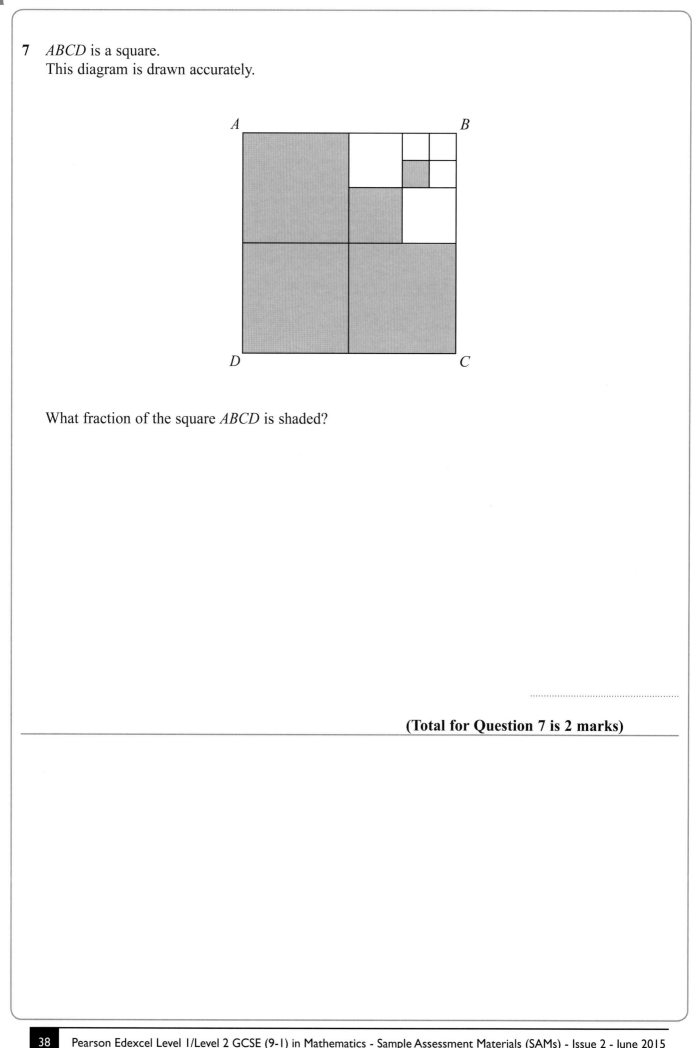

What fraction of the square *ABCD* is shaded?

....

(Total for Question 7 is 2 marks)

© Pearson Education Limited 2015

8 Sam and Max work in a shop from Monday to Friday.

Sam draws a graph to show the number of TVs they each sell.

Write down **three** things that are wrong with this graph.

1 ....

....

2 ....

....

3 ....

....

(Total for Question 8 is 3 marks)

9 Here is a list of numbers

12   19   12   15   11   15   12   13   17

Find the median.

....

(Total for Question 9 is 2 marks)

10 (a) Rob buys p packets of plain crisps and c packets of cheese crisps.

Write down an expression for the total number of packets of crisps Rob buys.

....

(1)

(b) Solve $3x - 5 = 9$

$x =$ ....

(2)

(Total for Question 10 is 3 marks)

11 Adam says,

"When you multiply an even number by an odd number the answer is always an odd number."

(a) Write down an example to show Adam is wrong.

....

(1)

Betty says,

"When you multiply two prime numbers together the answer is always an odd number."

(b) Betty is wrong.
Explain why.

....

....

(2)

(Total for Question 11 is 3 marks)

12 You can use the information in the table to convert between kilometres and miles.

miles	0	5	20	40
kilometres	0	8	32	64

(a) Use this information to draw a conversion graph.

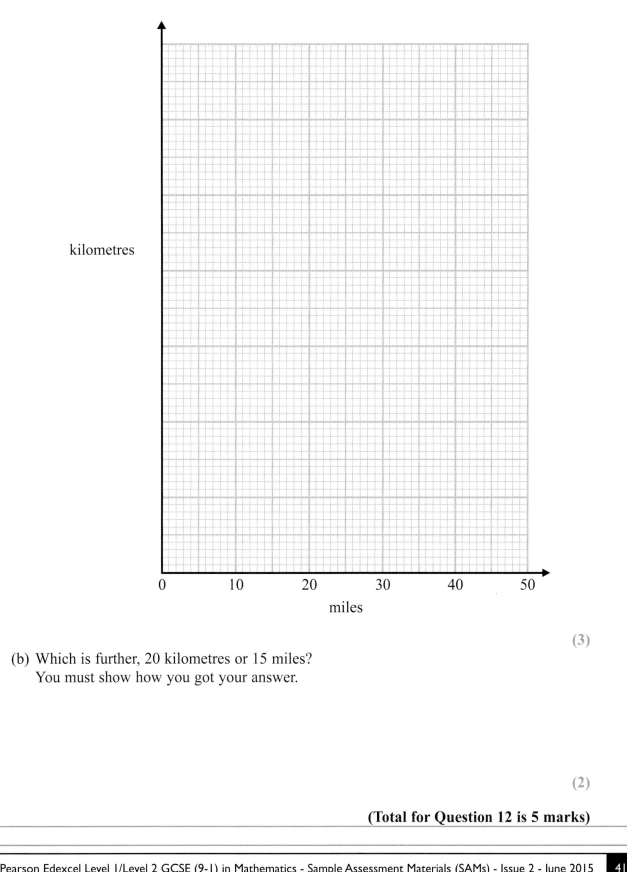

(3)

(b) Which is further, 20 kilometres or 15 miles?
   You must show how you got your answer.

(2)

(Total for Question 12 is 5 marks)

© Pearson Education Limited 2015

13

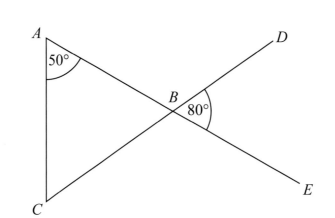

ABE and *CBD* are straight lines.

Show that triangle *ABC* is an isosceles triangle.
Give a reason for each stage of your working.

(Total for Question 13 is 4 marks)

Pearson Edexcel Level 1/Level 2 GCSE (9-1) in Mathematics - Sample Assessment Materials (SAMs) - Issue 2 - June 2015
© Pearson Education Limited 2015

14 The diagram shows a tank in the shape of a cuboid.
It also shows a container in the shape of a cuboid.

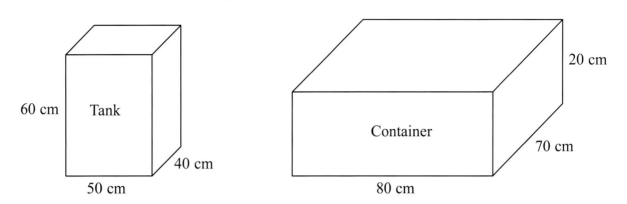

60 cm | Tank

50 cm

40 cm

Container

20 cm

70 cm

80 cm

The tank is full of oil.
The container is empty.

35% of the oil from the tank is spilled.
The rest of the oil from the tank is put into the container.

Work out the height of the oil in the container.
Give your answer to an appropriate degree of accuracy.

.... cm

(Total for Question 14 is 5 marks)

© Pearson Education Limited 2015

15 The diagram below represents two towns on a map.

Diagram **accurately** drawn

×
Towey

×
Worsley

Scale: 1 cm represents 3 kilometres.

Work out the distance, in kilometres, between Towey and Worsley.

....km

(Total for Question 15 is 2 marks)

16 Find the Highest Common Factor (HCF) of 24 and 60

....

(Total for Question 16 is 2 marks)

Pearson Edexcel Level 1/Level 2 GCSE (9-1) in Mathematics - Sample Assessment Materials (SAMs) - Issue 2 - June 2015
© Pearson Education Limited 2015

17 Soap powder is sold in three sizes of box.

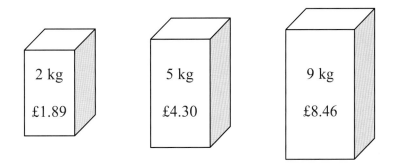

A 2 kg box of soap powder costs £1.89
A 5 kg box of soap powder costs £4.30
A 9 kg box of soap powder costs £8.46

Which size of box of soap powder is the best value for money?
You must show how you get your answer.

(Total for Question 17 is 3 marks)

© Pearson Education Limited 2015

18 $f = 5x + 2y$

  $x = 3$ and $y = -2$

  Find the value of f.

....

(Total for Question 18 is 2 marks)

19 Jane made some almond biscuits which she sold at a fete.

  She had:
  5 kg of flour
  3 kg of butter
  2.5 kg of icing sugar
  320 g of almonds

  Here is the list of ingredients for making 24 almond biscuits.

Ingredients for 24 almond biscuits
150 g flour
100 g butter
75 g icing sugar
10 g almonds

  Jane made as many almond biscuits as she could, using the ingredients she had.

  Work out how many almond biscuits she made.

....

(Total for Question 19 is 3 marks)

Pearson Edexcel Level 1/Level 2 GCSE (9-1) in Mathematics - Sample Assessment Materials (SAMs) - Issue 2 - June 2015
© Pearson Education Limited 2015

20 (a) Factorise $3f + 9$

....
(1)

(b) Factorise $x^2 - 2x - 15$

....
(2)

(Total for Question 20 is 3 marks)

21 $q = \dfrac{p}{r} + s$

Make p the subject of this formula.

....

(Total for Question 21 is 2 marks)

22 A tin of varnish costs £15

A rectangular floor has dimensions 6 m by 11 m.
The floor is going to be covered in varnish.

11 m

6 m

Helen assumes that each tin of this varnish covers an area of 12 m².

(a) Using Helen's assumption, work out the cost of buying the varnish for this floor.

£ ....

(4)

Helen finds that each tin of varnish covers less than 12 m².

(b) Explain how this might affect the number of tins she needs to buy.

....

....

(1)

(Total for Question 22 is 5 marks)

23 Frank, Mary and Seth shared some sweets in the ratio 4 : 5 : 7
Seth got 18 more sweets than Frank.

Work out the total number of sweets they shared.

....

(Total for Question 23 is 3 marks)

---

24 *PQR* is a right-angled triangle.

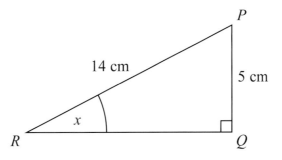

Work out the size of the angle marked *x*.
Give your answer correct to 1 decimal place.

....°

(Total for Question 24 is 2 marks)

25 Here are the first four terms of an arithmetic sequence.

$$6 \qquad 10 \qquad 14 \qquad 18$$

(a) Write an expression, in terms of n, for the nth term of this sequence.

....

(2)

The nth term of a different arithmetic sequence is $3n + 5$

(b) Is 108 a term of this sequence?
   Show how you get your answer.

(2)

(Total for Question 25 is 4 marks)

Pearson Edexcel Level 1/Level 2 GCSE (9-1) in Mathematics - Sample Assessment Materials (SAMs) - Issue 2 - June 2015
© Pearson Education Limited 2015

26 Axel and Lethna are driving along a motorway.

They see a road sign.
The road sign shows the distance to Junction 8
It also shows the average time drivers take to get to Junction 8

> To Junction 8
> 30 miles
> 26 minutes

The speed limit on the motorway is 70 mph.

Lethna says

"We will have to drive faster than the speed limit to drive 30 miles in 26 minutes."

Is Lethna right?
You must show how you get your answer.

(Total for Question 26 is 3 marks)

27 The table shows some information about the foot lengths of 40 adults.

Foot length (f cm)	Number of adults
$16 \leqslant f < 18$	3
$18 \leqslant f < 20$	6
$20 \leqslant f < 22$	10
$22 \leqslant f < 24$	12
$24 \leqslant f < 26$	9

(a) Write down the modal class interval.

....

(1)

(b) Calculate an estimate for the mean foot length.

.... cm

(3)

(Total for Question 27 is 4 marks)

28 Triangles *ABD* and *BCD* are right-angled triangles.

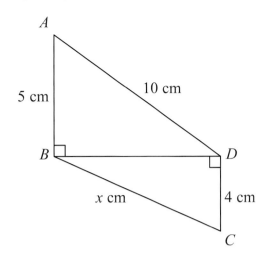

Work out the value of *x*.
Give your answer correct to 2 decimal places.

....

(Total for Question 28 is 4 marks)

29 Here is a probability tree diagram.

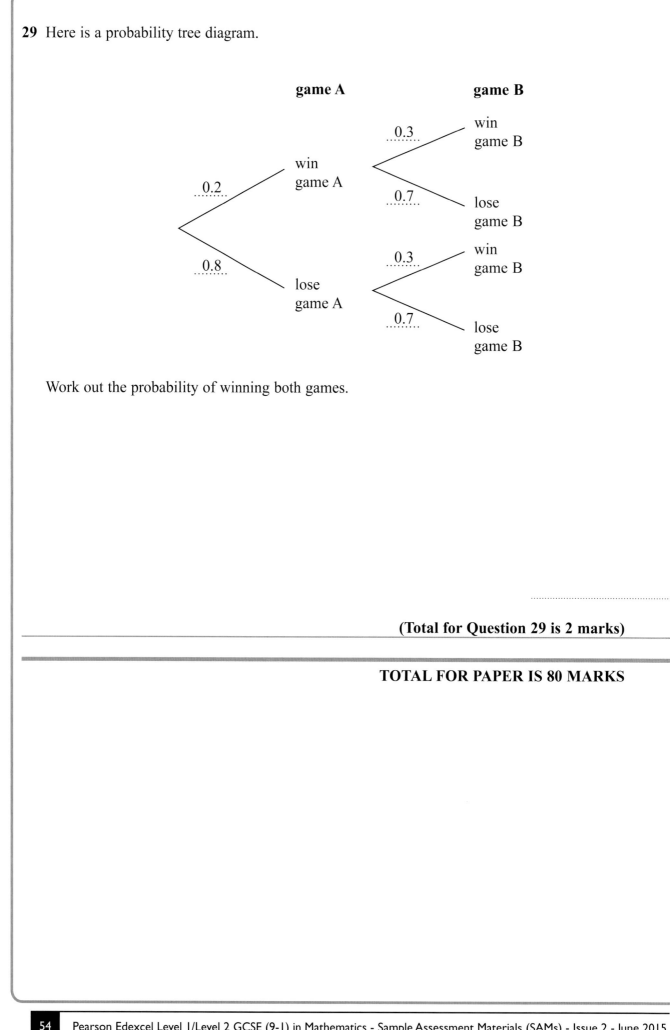

Work out the probability of winning both games.

....

Paper 1MA1: 2F

Question	Working	Answer		Notes
1		6.66	B1	cao
2		0.4375	B1	cao
3		27 or 64	B1	cao
4		7.3225	M1	for 5.5225 **or** 1.8
			A1	cao
5		²⁄₃	B1	oe
6		eg. 1, 2, 18	P1	Starts process eg. Lists at least 2 multiples from 9,18,27,36,45 **or** lists at least 2 factors from 1, 2, 4, 5, 8, 10, 20, 40
			P1	Continues process eg. gives a set of numbers whose sum is greater than 20 but less than 30 but numbers may not all be appropriate factors/multiples
			A1	Gives 3 numbers that meet all the criteria

© Pearson Education Limited 2015

Question	Working	Answer		Notes
7		$\dfrac{53}{64}$	P1	for interpreting information e.g. recognising that the shaded area = $\dfrac{3}{4} + \left(\dfrac{1}{4} \times \dfrac{1}{4}\right) + \left(\dfrac{1}{4} \times \dfrac{1}{4} \times \dfrac{1}{4}\right)$ or adding in lines to diagram to show 64ths
			A1	cao
8			C1	Any one correct statement eg. No key, y axis label, 4 missing on y axis
			C1	Any 2nd correct statement
			C1	Any 3rd correct statement
9		13	M1	Puts numbers in order or clear attempt to find 5th number **or** $(9+1)/2$ **or** selects 11
			A1	
10 (a)		$p + c$	B1	
(b)		$\dfrac{14}{3}$	M1	adds 5 to both sides of equation
			A1	oe
11 (a)		eg. $2 \times 5 = 10$	B1	example given
(b)		explanation	P1	two prime numbers identified
			C1	conclusion which also shows at least one calculation with prime numbers or identifies one of the prime numbers as 2.

Paper 1MA1: 2F

Question		Working	Answer		Notes
12	(a)		graph	C1	introduce a scale for the y axis
				C1	plots at least 2 points correctly
				C1	fully correct and complete graph
	(b)		15 miles (supported)	M1	reads off graph eg 20 km = 12-13 miles or 15 miles = 24 km or uses table
				C1	states 15 miles (24 km) with appropriate evidence
13			shown	B1	$ABC = 80$
				M1	$180 - 80° - 50°$
				A1	$ACB = 50$
				C1	statement that since $ACB = CAB = 50°$ with reasons eg Vertically opposite angles are equal, Angles in a triangle add up to 180°, The exterior angle of a triangle is equal to the sum of the interior opposite angles; Base angles of an isosceles triangle are equal.
14			13.9	P1	finds the volume of a cuboid eg 50×40×60 (=120000)
				P1	finds 35% of the oil from the cuboid eg 120000 × 0.35 oe (=42000)
				P1	removes 35% of oil from cuboid eg 120000 − 42000 (=78000)
				P1	division to find missing side length eg 78000÷(80×70) or 13.928...
				A1	for answer to an appropriate degree of accuracy eg (13.9 or 14 or 10)

Paper 1MA1: 2F				
Question	Working	Answer		Notes
15		22.5	M1	interpret information eg use the scale
			A1	
16		12	M1	Starts to list factors of writes at least one number in terms of prime factors **or** identifies a common factor other than 1
			A1	cao
17	£ per kg: $1.89 \div 2 = 0.945$ (94.5); $4.30 \div 5 = 0.86$ (86); $8.46 \div 9 = 0.94$ (94) kg per £: $2 \div 1.89 = 1.058(2...)$; $5 \div 4.30 = 1.162(79...)$; $9 \div 8.46 = 1.0638(297...)$ Price per 90 kg: $1.89 \times 45 = 85.05$; $4.30 \times 18 = 77.4(0)$; $8.46 \times 10 = 84.6(0)$	5 kg (supported)	P1	for a process (for at least two boxes) of division of price by quantity or division of quantity by price or a complete method to find price of same quantity or to find quantity of same price
			P1	for a complete process to give values that can be used for comparison of all 3 boxes
			C1	for 5 kg and correct values that can be used for comparison for all 3 boxes and a comparison of their values
18		11	M1	process of substitution demonstrated eg $5 \times 3 + 2 \times -2$
			A1	cao

Pearson Edexcel Level 1/Level 2 GCSE (9-1) in Mathematics - Sample Assessment Materials (SAMs) - Issue 2 - June 2015
© Pearson Education Limited 2015

Question	Working	Answer		Notes
19		720	P1	attempt to find the maximum biscuits for one of the ingredients e.g. $5000 \div 15$ (=33.3...) or $2500 \div 75$ (=33.3...) or $3000 \div 100$ (=30) or $320 \div 10$ (=32)
			P1	for identifying butter as the limiting factor or 30×24 (=720) seen
			A1	
20 (a)		$3(f+3)$	B1	cao
(b)		$(x-5)(x+3)$	M1	for $(x \pm 5)(x \pm 3)$
			A1	cao
21		$p = qr - sr$	M1	for multiplying all 3 terms by r or isolating p/r term
			A1	oe
22 (a)		90	P1	for the process of finding an area eg 6×11 (=66)
			P1	(dep on area calculation) for the process of working out the number of tins eg "66" $\div 12$ (=5.5 or 6 tins)
			P1	for the process of working out the cost eg "6" tins $\times$ £15
			A1	cao
(b)		reason	C1	she might need to buy more tins

© Pearson Education Limited 2015

Question	Working	Answer		Notes
23		96	P1	a strategy to start to solve the problem eg $18 \div (7-4)$ $(=6)$
			P1	for completing the process of solution eg "6" $\times (4 + 5 + 7)$
			A1	cao
24		20.9	M1	correct recall of appropriate formula eg $\sin x = \dfrac{5}{14}$
			A1	for 20.9(248…)
25 (a)		$4n+2$	M1	start to deduce nth term from information given eg $4n+k$ where $k \neq 2$
			A1	cao
(b)		No (supported)	M1	start to method that could lead to a deduction eg uses inverse operations
			C1	for a convincing argument eg 34 is 107 so NO; $(108-5) \div 3$ is not an integer
26		conclusion	P1	$30 \div 70$ $(=0.428)$ — $26 \div 60$ $(=0.4333…)$ — $30 \div 26$ $(=1.153…)$
		(supported)	P1	$60 \times$ "0.428…" — $70 \times$ "0.4333…" — $60 \times$ "1.153…"
			C1	for conclusion linked to 25.7 mins, 30.3 miles or 69.2 mph

Pearson Edexcel Level 1/Level 2 GCSE (9-1) in Mathematics - Sample Assessment Materials (SAMs) - Issue 2 - June 2015
© Pearson Education Limited 2015

Question		Working	Answer		Notes
27	(a)		$22 \le f < 24$	B1	
	(b)		21.9	M1	$x \times f$ using midpoints
				M1	(dep on previous mark) "$x \times f$" ÷ 40
				A1	accept 22 if working seen
28			9.54	P1	$10^2 - 5^2 \ (=75)$
				P1	"75" $+ 4^2 \ (=91)$
				P1	$\sqrt{(10^2 - 5^2 + 4^2)}$
				A1	$9.53 - 9.54$
29			0.06	M1	for 0.2 and 0.3
				A1	cao

© Pearson Education Limited 2015

Pearson Edexcel Level 1/Level 2 GCSE (9-1) in Mathematics - Sample Assessment Materials (SAMs) - Issue 2 - June 2015
© Pearson Education Limited 2015

Write your name here

Surname		Other names	

Pearson Edexcel
Level 1/Level 2 GCSE (9 - 1)

Centre Number

Candidate Number

Mathematics

Paper 3 (Calculator)

Foundation Tier

Sample Assessment Materials - Issue 2
Time: 1 hour 30 minutes

Paper Reference
1MA1/3F

You must have: Ruler graduated in centimetres and millimetres, protractor, pair of compasses, pen, HB pencil, eraser, calculator.

Total Marks

Instructions

- Use **black** ink or ball-point pen.
- **Fill in the boxes** at the top of this page with your name, centre number and candidate number.
- Answer **all** questions.
- Answer the questions in the spaces provided
  - *there may be more space than you need.*
- **Calculators may be used.**
- If your calculator does not have a π button, take the value of π to be 3.142 unless the question instructs otherwise.
- Diagrams are **NOT** accurately drawn, unless otherwise indicated.
- You must **show all your working out**.

Information

- The total mark for this paper is 80
- The marks for **each** question are shown in brackets
  - *use this as a guide as to how much time to spend on each question.*

Advice

- Read each question carefully before you start to answer it.
- Keep an eye on the time.
- Try to answer every question.
- Check your answers if you have time at the end.

Turn over ▶

S48575A
©2015 Pearson Education Ltd.
6/4/7/4/6/6/6/

Answer ALL questions.

Write your answers in the spaces provided.

You must write down all the stages in your working.

1   Write 2148 correct to the nearest 100

....

(Total for Question 1 is 1 mark)

2   (a) Simplify $8x - 3x + 2x$

....

(1)

(b) Simplify $4y \times 2y$

....

(1)

(Total for Question 2 is 2 marks)

3   There are 6760 people at at a rugby match.
    3879 of the people are men.
    1241 of the people are women.

    $\dfrac{1}{4}$ of the children are girls.

    Work out how many boys are at the rugby match.

....

(Total for Question 3 is 3 marks)

Pearson Edexcel Level 1/Level 2 GCSE (9-1) in Mathematics - Sample Assessment Materials (SAMs) - Issue 2 - June 2015
© Pearson Education Limited 2015

4 Here is a grid showing the points *A*, *B* and *C*.

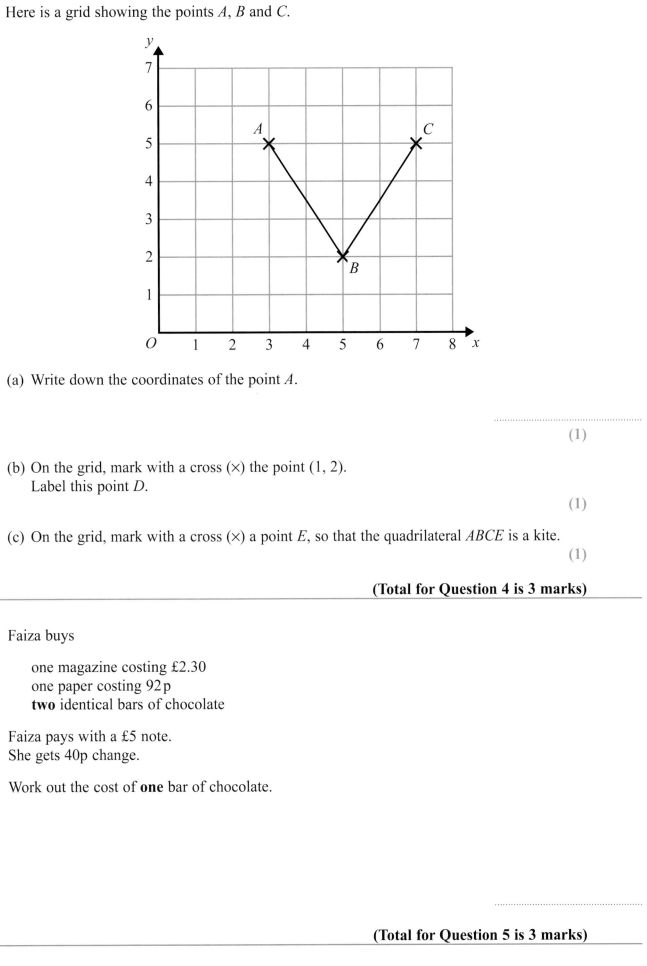

(a) Write down the coordinates of the point *A*.

....

(1)

(b) On the grid, mark with a cross (×) the point (1, 2).
Label this point *D*.

(1)

(c) On the grid, mark with a cross (×) a point *E*, so that the quadrilateral *ABCE* is a kite.

(1)

(Total for Question 4 is 3 marks)

---

5 Faiza buys

    one magazine costing £2.30
    one paper costing 92 p
    two identical bars of chocolate

Faiza pays with a £5 note.
She gets 40p change.

Work out the cost of **one** bar of chocolate.

....

(Total for Question 5 is 3 marks)

© Pearson Education Limited 2015

6 The bar chart gives information about the numbers of students in the four Year 11 classes at Trowton School.

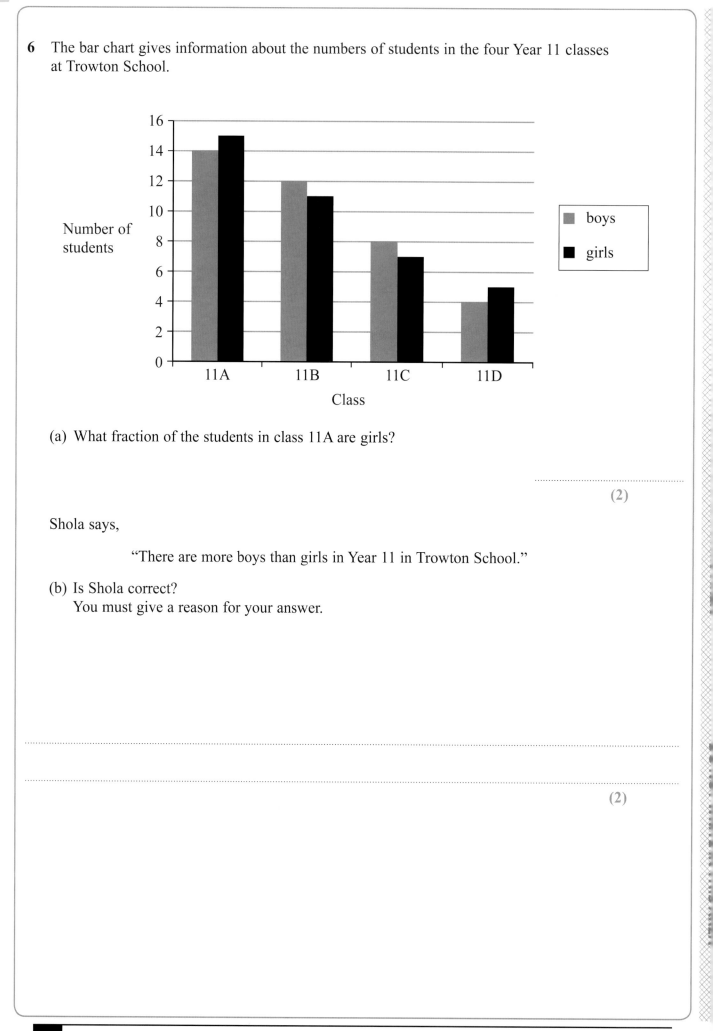

(a) What fraction of the students in class 11A are girls?

....

(2)

Shola says,

  "There are more boys than girls in Year 11 in Trowton School."

(b) Is Shola correct?
   You must give a reason for your answer.

....

....

(2)

The pie chart gives information about the 76 students in the same four Year 11 classes at Trowton School.

Number of students in Year 11 of Trowton School

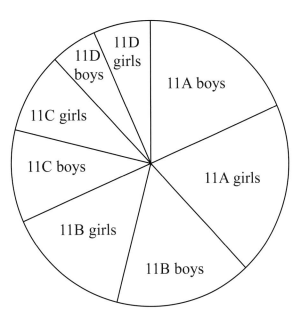

Tolu says,

"It is more difficult to find out the numbers of students in each class from the pie chart than from the bar chart."

(c) Is Tolu correct?
You must give a reason for your answer.

....

....

(1)

(Total for Question 6 is 5 marks)

7 Here is a number machine.

$$\text{input} \longrightarrow \boxed{\times 3} \longrightarrow \boxed{-4} \longrightarrow \text{output}$$

(a) Work out the **output** when the input is 4

....

(1)

(b) Work out the **input** when the output is 11

....

(2)

(c) Show that there is a value of the input for which the input and the output have the same value.

(2)

(Total for Question 7 is 5 marks)

Pearson Edexcel Level 1/Level 2 GCSE (9-1) in Mathematics - Sample Assessment Materials (SAMs) - Issue 2 - June 2015
© Pearson Education Limited 2015

8 1 yard is 36 inches.
10 cm is an approximation for 4 inches.

Work out an approximation for the number of cm in 2 yards.

....

9 Work out 234% of 150

....

10 Here are four numbers.

$$0.43 \qquad \frac{3}{7} \qquad 43.8\% \qquad \frac{7}{16}$$

Write these numbers in order of size.
Start with the smallest number.

....

(Total for Question 10 is 2 marks)

11 Here is a list of five numbers.

$$14 \qquad 15 \qquad 16 \qquad 17 \qquad 18$$

From the list,

(i) write down the prime number,

....

(ii) write down the square number.

....

(Total for Question 11 is 2 marks)

12 Here is a star shape.

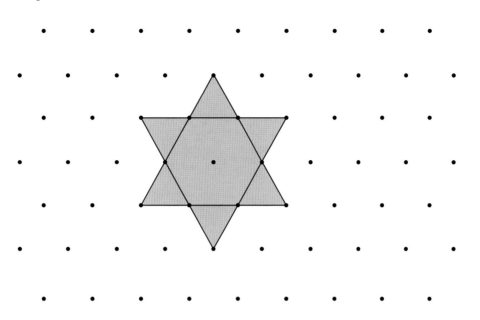

The star shape is made from a regular hexagon and six congruent equilateral triangles.

The area of the star shape is 96 cm².

Work out the area of the regular hexagon.

.... cm²

(Total for Question 12 is 2 marks)

© Pearson Education Limited 2015

13

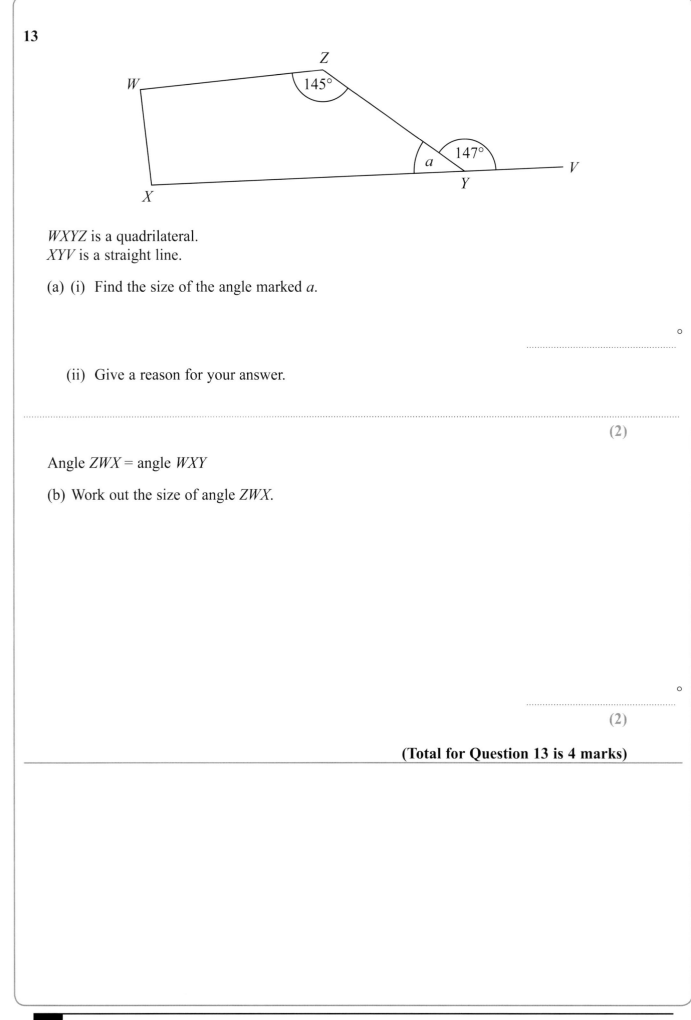

WXYZ is a quadrilateral.
XYV is a straight line.

(a) (i) Find the size of the angle marked *a*.

.... °

(ii) Give a reason for your answer.

....

(2)

Angle *ZWX* = angle *WXY*

(b) Work out the size of angle *ZWX*.

.... °

(2)

(Total for Question 13 is 4 marks)

14 The total weight of 3 tins of beans and 4 jars of jam is 2080 g.
The total weight of 5 tins of beans is 2000 g.

Work out the weight of 1 tin of beans and the weight of 1 jar of jam.

tin of beans..................................... g

jar of jam..................................... g

(Total for Question 14 is 4 marks)

© Pearson Education Limited 2015

15 There are 25 boys and 32 girls in a club.

$\frac{2}{5}$ of the boys and $\frac{1}{2}$ of the girls walk to the club.

The club leader picks at random a child from the children who walk to the club.

Work out the probability that this child is a boy.

....

(Total for Question 15 is 3 marks)

Pearson Edexcel Level 1/Level 2 GCSE (9-1) in Mathematics - Sample Assessment Materials (SAMs) - Issue 2 - June 2015
© Pearson Education Limited 2015

16 Change 72 km/h into m/s.

....m / s

(Total for Question 16 is 3 marks)

17 Here is a rectangle made of card.

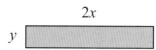

The measurements in the diagram are in centimetres.

Lily fits four of these rectangles together to make a frame.

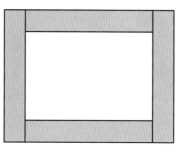

The perimeter of the inside of the frame is P cm.

(a) Show that $P = 8x - 4y$

(2)

Magda says,

"When x and y are whole numbers, P is always a multiple of 4."

(b) Is Magda correct?
You must give a reason for your answer.

....

....

(2)

(Total for Question 17 is 4 marks)

18 The diagram shows a trapezium *ABCD* and two identical semicircles.

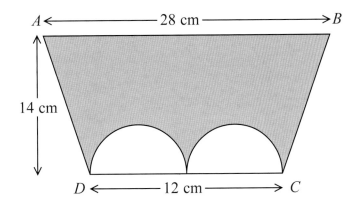

The centre of each semicircle is on *DC*.

Work out the area of the shaded region.
Give your answer correct to 3 significant figures.

.... cm²

(Total for Question 18 is 4 marks)

19 Asif is going on holiday to Turkey.

The exchange rate is £1 = 3.5601 lira.

Asif changes £550 to lira.

(a) Work out how many lira he should get.
Give your answer to the nearest lira.

.... lira

(2)

Asif sees a pair of shoes in Turkey.
The shoes cost 210 lira.

Asif does not have a calculator.
He uses £2 = 7 lira to work out the approximate cost of the shoes in pounds.

(b) Use £2 = 7 lira to show that the approximate cost of the shoes is £60

(2)

(c) Is using £2 = 7 lira instead of using £1 = 3.5601 lira a sensible start to Asif's method to work out the cost of the shoes in pounds?

You must give a reason for your answer.

....

....

(1)

(Total for Question 19 is 5 marks)

20 Here are the first six terms of a Fibonacci sequence.

$$1 \quad 1 \quad 2 \quad 3 \quad 5 \quad 8$$

The rule to continue a Fibonacci sequence is,

the next term in the sequence is the sum of the two previous terms.

(a) Find the 9th term of this sequence.

....

(1)

The first three terms of a different Fibonacci sequence are

$$a \quad b \quad a + b$$

(b) Show that the 6th term of this sequence is $3a + 5b$

(2)

Given that the 3rd term is 7 and the 6th term is 29,

(c) find the value of a and the value of b.

$a =$ ....

$b =$ ....

(3)

(Total for Question 20 is 6 marks)

© Pearson Education Limited 2015

21 In a survey, the outside temperature and the number of units of electricity used for heating were recorded for ten homes.

The scatter diagram shows this information.

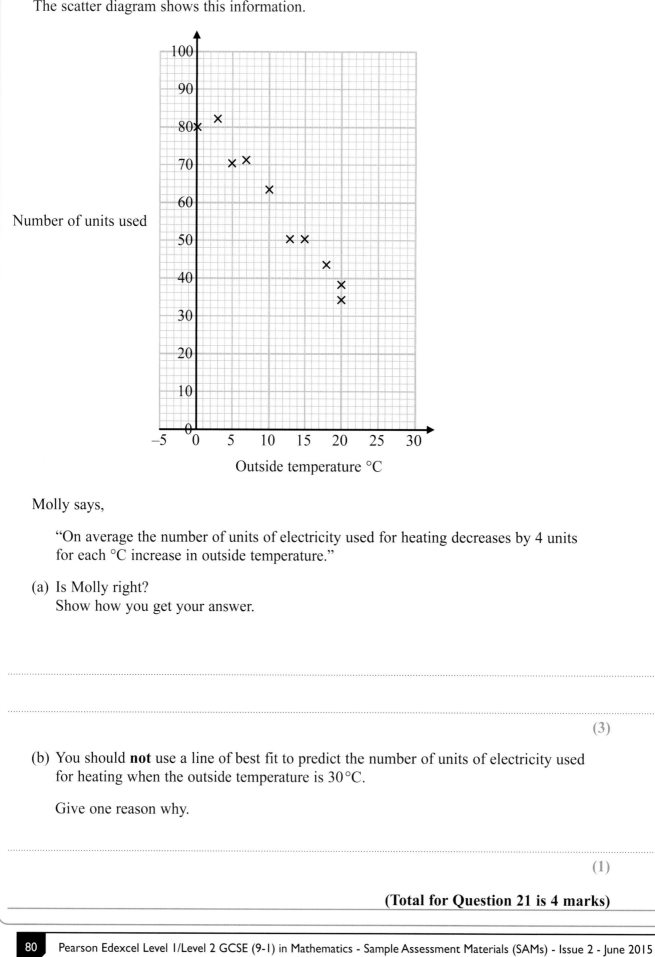

Molly says,

"On average the number of units of electricity used for heating decreases by 4 units for each °C increase in outside temperature."

(a) Is Molly right?
Show how you get your answer.

....

....

(3)

(b) You should **not** use a line of best fit to predict the number of units of electricity used for heating when the outside temperature is 30°C.

Give one reason why.

....

(1)

(Total for Question 21 is 4 marks)

22 Henry is thinking of having a water meter.

These are the two ways he can pay for the water he uses.

Water Meter

A charge of £28.20 per year

plus

91.22p for every cubic metre of water used

1 cubic metre = 1000 litres

No Water Meter

A charge of £107 per year

Henry uses an average of 180 litres of water each day.

Use this information to determine whether or not Henry should have a water meter.

(Total for Question 22 is 5 marks)

DO NOT WRITE IN THIS AREA

© Pearson Education Limited 2015

23 A and B are two companies.

The table shows some information about the sales of each company and the number of workers for each company in 2004 and in 2014

	Company A		Company B	
	Sales (£ millions)	Number of workers	Sales (£ millions)	Number of workers
2004	320	2960	48	605
2014	388	3200	57	640

(a) Work out the percentage increase in sales from 2004 to 2014 for Company A.

.... %

(2)

(b) Which company had the most sales per worker in 2014, Company A or Company B? You must show how you get your answer.

(3)

(Total for Question 23 is 5 marks)

TOTAL FOR PAPER IS 80 MARKS

Pearson Edexcel Level 1/Level 2 GCSE (9-1) in Mathematics - Sample Assessment Materials (SAMs) - Issue 2 - June 2015
© Pearson Education Limited 2015

Paper 1MA1: 3F

Question		Working	Answer		Notes
1			2100	B1	
2	(a)		$7x$	B1	
	(b)		$8y^2$	B1	
3			1230	P1	for start to process eg. $6760 - 3879 - 1241$ $(=1640)$
				P1	for use of fraction eg. "1640"÷4 or $1 - \dfrac{1}{4} \left(= \dfrac{3}{4} \right)$
				A1	
4	(a)		(3, 5)	B1	
	(b)		Plotted	B1	
	(c)		eg. (5,6) plotted	B1	
5		$(500 - 230 - 92 - 40) \div 2$	69p	P1	for start to process eg. $230 + 92$ or $500 - 40$
				P1	for complete process
				A1	for 69p or £0.69

© Pearson Education Limited 2015

Paper 1MA1: 3F

Question		Working	Answer		Notes
6	(a)		$\dfrac{15}{29}$	M1	for $\dfrac{15}{a}$ where $a > 15$ or $\dfrac{b}{29}$ where $b < 29$ **or** correct fraction for girls from a different class
				A1	
	(b)	11A +1G, 11B −1G 11C −1G, 11D + 1G	No + reason	M1	For complete method to find the sum of the signed differences in numbers of boys and girls or the totals of boys and girls in year 11
				C1	'No' with correct argument eg. there are 38 boys and 38 girls
	(c)		Yes + reason	C1	'Yes' with eg as many calculations using the angles would be required oe
7	(a)		8	B1	
	(b)	$11 + 4 = 15$ $15 \div 3 = 5$	5	M1	Start of method
				A1	
	(c)		2	M1	For complete method that leads to answer e.g table of values or x $= 3x - 4$
				C1	For 2 or for statement that the equation has a unique solution
8			180	M1	For start to method e.g. $36 \div 4 (= 9)$ or 2×36
				M1	For complete method to find no of cm in 1 yard **or** in 2 yards
				A1	
9			351	M1	for 2.34×150 oe
				A1	

Table for 7(c):

in	0	1	2	3	4
out	-4	-1	2	5	8

Pearson Edexcel Level 1/Level 2 GCSE (9-1) in Mathematics - Sample Assessment Materials (SAMs) - Issue 2 - June 2015
© Pearson Education Limited 2015

Question	Working	Answer		Notes
10	0.43, 0.428..., 0.438. 0.4375	$\frac{3}{7}$, 0.43, $\frac{7}{16}$, 43.8%,	M1	Converts numbers to common format e.g decimals to at least 3 d.p.
			A1	
11 (i)		17	B1	
(ii)	1	16	B1	
12		48	P1	For start to process eg.96 ÷ 12 **or** 96 ÷ 2
			A1	cao
13 (a)(i) (ii)		33 The sum of the angles on a straight line is 180	B1 B1	The sum of the angles on a straight line is 180°
(b)	$(360 - 33 - 145) \div 2$	91	P1 A1	For a correct process to find angle ZWX
14	$2000 \div 5 = 400$ $2080 - 3 \times 400 = 880$ $880 \div 4$	400, 220	B1 P1 P1 A1	for 400 (weight of beans) Process to find total weight of 4 jars of jam Process to find weight of 1 jar of jam
15	$25 \div 5 \times 2 = 10$ $32 \div 2 = 16$ $\dfrac{10}{10+16}$	$\dfrac{10}{26}$	P1 P1 A1	Process to find number of boys walking and number of girls walking Complete process to find probability $\dfrac{10}{26}$ oe

Paper 1MA1: 3F

Question		Working	Answer		Notes
16			20	M1	for conversion of km to metres or hours to minutes
				M1	for conversion of hours to seconds
				A1	cao
17	(a)	$2x + 2x - 2y + 2x + 2x - 2y$	Shown	M1	For method to acquire correct inside lengths
				C1	For completion
	(b)	$8x$ and $4y$ are multiples of 4 Their difference must be a multiple of 4 Or $4(2x - y)$ is a multiple of 4	Shown	M1	For method to start argument eg. factorise expression
				C1	For complete argument
18			252	P1	For start to process eg. radius $= 12 \div 4$ ($=3$)
				M1	Method to find area of trapezium or semicircle or circle
				P1	Process to find area of the shaded region
				A1	$251.7 - 252$
19	(a)	550×3.5601	1958	M1	550×3.5601
				A1	
	(b)	$210 \div 7 \times 2 = 30 \times 2$ Or $60 \div 2 = 30$ and $30 \times 7 = 210$	Shown	M1	For correct method to convert cost in UK to lira or vice versa, using Asif's approximation
				C1	Shown with correct calculations
	(c)		Correct evaluation	C1	For an evaluation e.g. It is a sensible start to the method because he can do the calculations without a calculator and 3.5 lira to the £ is a good approximation

© Pearson Education Limited 2015

Question		Working	Answer		Notes
20	(a)	8, 13, 21,	34	B1	cao
	(b)	$a, b, a+b, a+2b, 2a+3b$	Shown	M1	Method to show by adding pairs of successive terms $a+2b, 2a+3b$ shown
				C1	
	(c)	$3a+5b=29$ $a+b=7$ $3a+3b=21$ $b=4, a=3$	$a=3$ $b=4$	P1	Process to set up two equations
				P1	Process to solve equations
				A1	
21	(a)	Draws LOBF Finds ht$\div$base $= \dfrac{85-20}{0-25} = -2.6$	No + reason	M1	Interpret question eg. draw line of best fit
				M1	Start to test eg. gradient e.g. $\dfrac{85-20}{0-25} = -2.6$
	(b)		The LOBF would have to be used outside the data	C1	Gradient within range $\pm(2-3)$ and 'no'
				C1	Convincing explanation
22			Have a water meter (from working with correct figures)	P1	Process to find number of litres eg. $180 \div 1000$
				P1	Full process to find cost per day
				P1	Full process to find total cost of water used per year (accept use of alternative time period for both options)
				P1	Full process with consistent units for total cost of water
				A1	Correct decision from correct figures (88.13154 or correct figure for their time period)

© Pearson Education Limited 2015

Paper 1MA1: 3F

Question		Working	Answer		Notes
23	(a)	$\dfrac{388-320}{320} \times 100 =$	21.25	M1	For a complete method
				A1	21.25%
	(b)	A 388 (million) ÷ 3200 = £0.12125 million (£121 250) B 57(million) ÷ 640 = £0.0890625 million (£89062.50)	Company A + evidence	M1	Method to find sales/person for A **or** B for 2014
				A1	£121 250 or £89062.50
				C1	Company A with £121 250 and £89062.50

© Pearson Education Limited 2015

Write your name here

Surname

Other names

Pearson Edexcel
Level 1/Level 2 GCSE (9 - 1)

Centre Number

Candidate Number

Mathematics

Paper 1 (Non-Calculator)

Higher Tier

Sample Assessment Materials – Issue 2
Time: 1 hour 30 minutes

Paper Reference
1MA1/1H

You must have: Ruler graduated in centimetres and millimetres, protractor, pair of compasses, pen, HB pencil, eraser.

Total Marks

Instructions

- Use **black** ink or ball-point pen.
- **Fill in the boxes** at the top of this page with your name, centre number and candidate number.
- Answer **all** questions.
- Answer the questions in the spaces provided
  – *there may be more space than you need.*
- **Calculators may not be used.**
- Diagrams are **NOT** accurately drawn, unless otherwise indicated.
- You must **show all your working out**.

Information

- The total mark for this paper is 80
- The marks for **each** question are shown in brackets
  – *use this as a guide as to how much time to spend on each question.*

Advice

- Read each question carefully before you start to answer it.
- Keep an eye on the time.
- Try to answer every question.
- Check your answers if you have time at the end.

Turn over ▶

S48572A
©2015 Pearson Education Ltd.
6/4/7/7/4/6/6/

PEARSON

Answer ALL questions.

Write your answers in the spaces provided.

You must write down all the stages in your working.

1   Work out 6.34×5.2

....

(Total for Question 1 is 3 marks)

2   Expand and simplify $(m + 7)(m + 3)$

....

(Total for Question 2 is 2 marks)

3

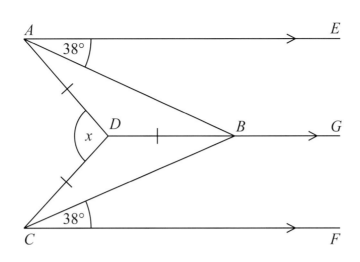

AE, *DBG* and *CF* are parallel.
DA = *DB* = *DC*.
Angle *EAB* = angle *BCF* = 38°

Work out the size of the angle marked *x*.
You must show your working.

.... °

(Total for Question 3 is 3 marks)

4   Gary drove from London to Sheffield.
    It took him 3 hours at an average speed of 80 km/h.

    Lyn drove from London to Sheffield.
    She took 5 hours.

    Assuming that Lyn
            drove along the same roads as Gary
        and did not take a break,

    (a) work out Lyn's average speed from London to Sheffield.

    ....km/h

    (3)

    (b) If Lyn did **not** drive along the same roads as Gary, explain how this could affect your
        answer to part (a).

    ....

    ....

    (1)

    (Total for Question 4 is 4 marks)

5 In a company, the ratio of the number of men to the number of women is $3:2$

40% of the men are under the age of 25
10% of the women are under the age of 25

What percentage of all the people in the company are under the age of 25?

....%

(Total for Question 5 is 4 marks)

6 The plan, front elevation and side elevation of a solid prism are drawn on a centimetre grid.

plan

front elevation   **side elevation**

In the space below, draw a sketch of the solid prism.
Write the dimensions of the prism on your sketch.

(Total for Question 6 is 2 marks)

7   There are 1200 students at a school.

Kate is helping to organise a party.
She is going to order pizza.

Kate takes a sample of 60 of the students at the school.
She asks each student to tell her **one** type of pizza they want.

The table shows information about her results.

Pizza	Number of students
ham	20
salami	15
vegetarian	8
margarita	17

Work out how much ham pizza Kate should order.
Write down any assumption you make **and** explain how this could affect your answer.

(Total for Question 7 is 3 marks)

8 Here is a parallelogram.

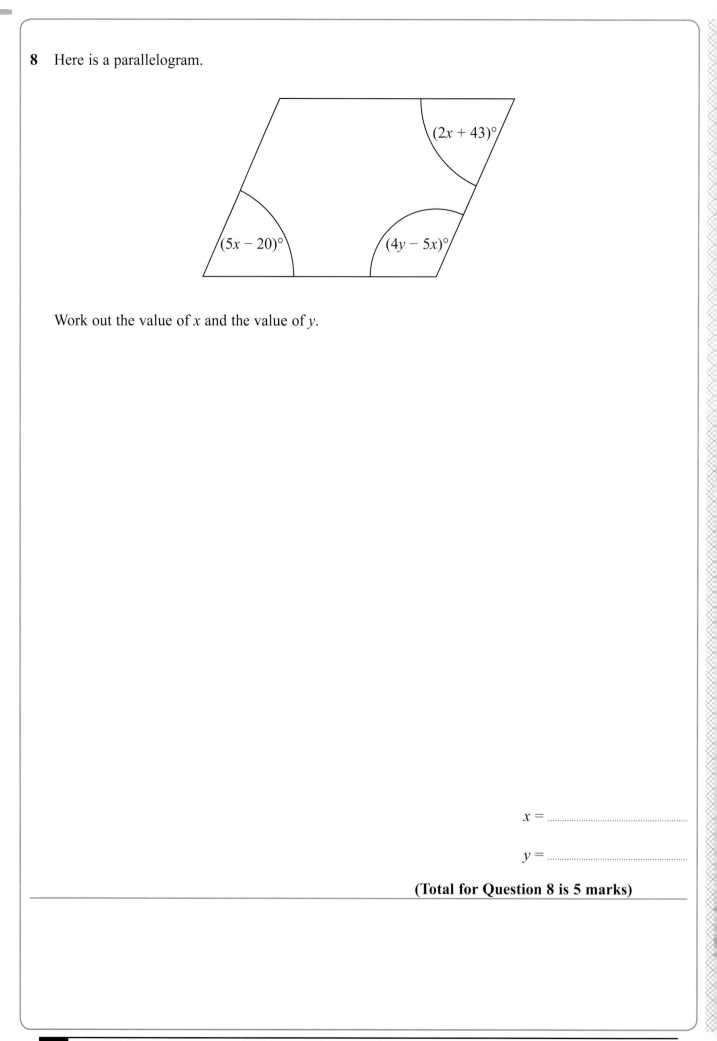

Work out the value of x and the value of y.

$x =$ ....

$y =$ ....

(Total for Question 8 is 5 marks)

9 Work out the value of $(9 \times 10^{-4}) \times (3 \times 10^7)$

Give your answer in standard form.

....

(Total for Question 9 is 2 marks)

10 (a) Write down the value of $64^{\frac{1}{2}}$

....

(1)

(b) Find the value of $\left(\dfrac{8}{125}\right)^{-\frac{2}{3}}$

....

(2)

(Total for Question 10 is 3 marks)

© Pearson Education Limited 2015

11 One uranium atom has a mass of 3.95×10^{-22} grams.

(a) Work out an estimate for the number of uranium atoms in 1 kg of uranium.

....

(3)

(b) Is your answer to (a) an underestimate or an overestimate?
Give a reason for your answer.

....

....

(1)

(Total for Question 11 is 4 marks)

Pearson Edexcel Level 1/Level 2 GCSE (9-1) in Mathematics - Sample Assessment Materials (SAMs) - Issue 2 - June 2015
© Pearson Education Limited 2015

12 Pressure $= \dfrac{\text{force}}{\text{area}}$

Find the pressure extered by a force of 900 newtons on an area of $60\,\text{cm}^2$.
Give your answer in newtons/m^2.

.... newtons/m^2

(Total for Question 12 is 2 marks)

13 Rectangle $ABCD$ is mathematically similar to rectangle $DAEF$.

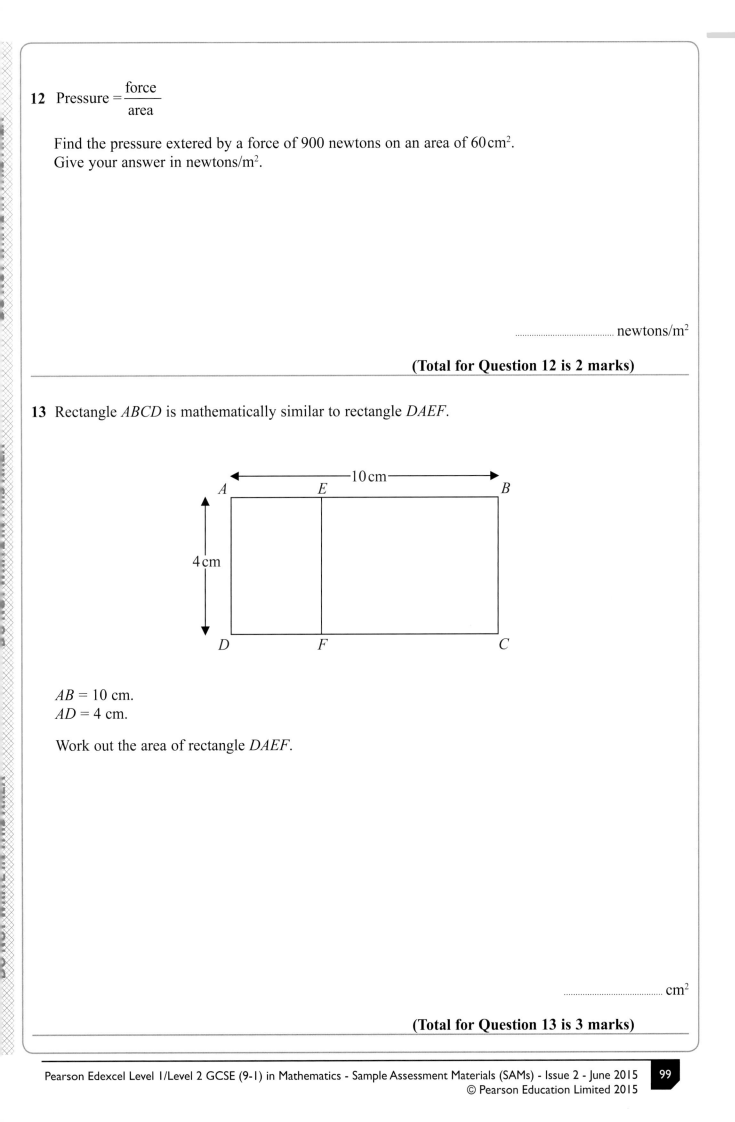

$AB = 10$ cm.
$AD = 4$ cm.

Work out the area of rectangle $DAEF$.

.... cm^2

(Total for Question 13 is 3 marks)

14 Ben played 15 games of basketball.
Here are the points he scored in each game.

   17   18   18   18   19   20   20   22   23   23   23   26   27   28   28

(a) Draw a box plot for this information.

(3)

Sam plays in the same 15 games of basketball.

The median number of points Sam scored is 23
The interquartile range of these points is 12
The range of these points is 20

(b) Who is more consistent at scoring points, Sam or Ben?
You must give a reason for your answer.

(2)

(Total for Question 14 is 5 marks)

© Pearson Education Limited 2015

15 In a shop, all normal prices are reduced by 20% to give the sale price.

The sale price of a TV set is then reduced by 30%.

Mary says,

"30 + 20 = 50, so this means that the normal price of the TV set has been reduced by 50%."

Is Mary right?
You must give a reason for your answer.

....

....

....

(Total for Question 15 is 2 marks)

16 Factorise fully $20x^2 - 5$

....

(Total for Question 16 is 2 marks)

17 Make a the subject of $\quad a + 3 = \dfrac{2a + 7}{r}$

....

(Total for Question 17 is 3 marks)

18 Solid **A** and solid **B** are mathematically similar.
The ratio of the surface area of solid **A** to the surface area of solid **B** is $4:9$

The volume of solid **B** is $405\,\text{cm}^3$.

Show that the volume of solid **A** is $120\,\text{cm}^3$.

(Total for Question 18 is 3 marks)

19 Solve $x^2 > 3x + 4$

(Total for Question 19 is 3 marks)

Pearson Edexcel Level 1/Level 2 GCSE (9-1) in Mathematics - Sample Assessment Materials (SAMs) - Issue 2 - June 2015
© Pearson Education Limited 2015

20

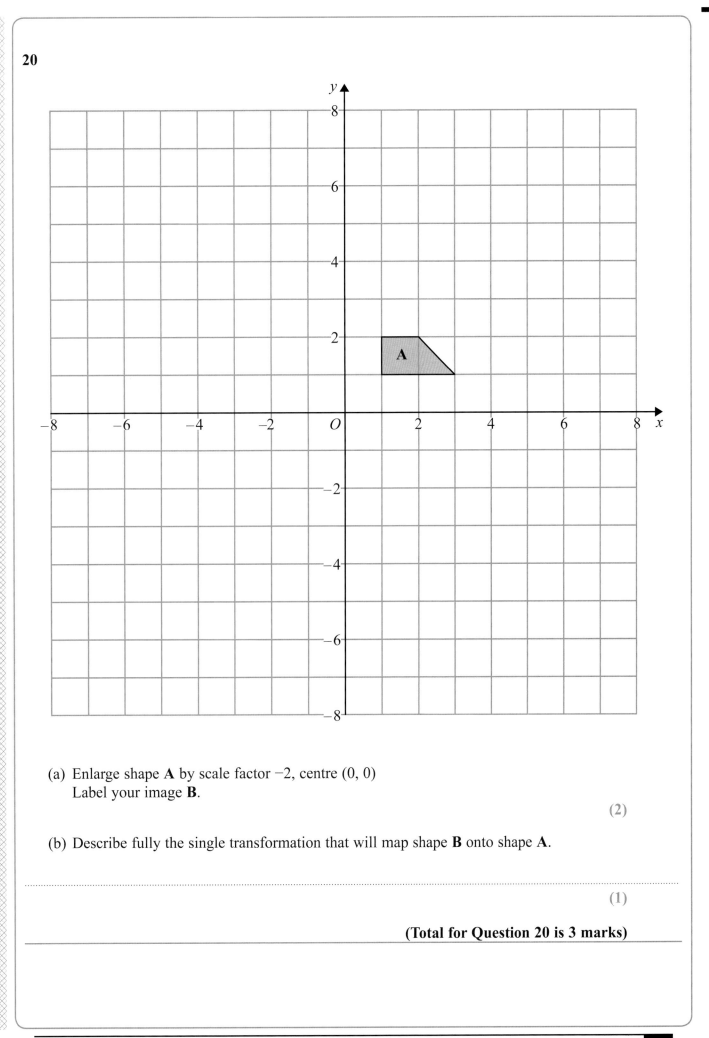

(a) Enlarge shape **A** by scale factor −2, centre (0, 0)
Label your image **B**.

(2)

(b) Describe fully the single transformation that will map shape **B** onto shape **A**.

....

(1)

(Total for Question 20 is 3 marks)

© Pearson Education Limited 2015

21 Here is a speed-time graph for a car journey.
The journey took 100 seconds.

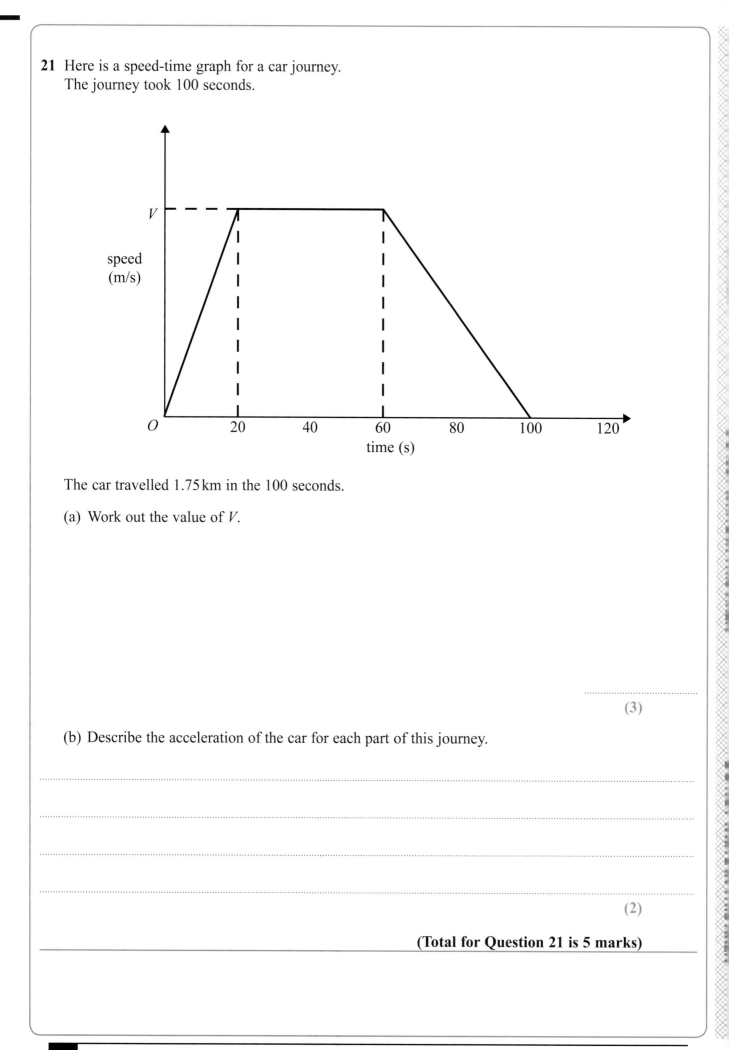

The car travelled 1.75 km in the 100 seconds.

(a) Work out the value of V.

....

(3)

(b) Describe the acceleration of the car for each part of this journey.

....

....

....

....

(2)

(Total for Question 21 is 5 marks)

© Pearson Education Limited 2015

22 Bhavna recorded the lengths of time, in hours, that some adults watched TV last week.

The table shows information about her results.

Length of time (*t* hours)	Frequency
$0 \leqslant t < 10$	6
$10 \leqslant t < 15$	8
$15 \leqslant t < 20$	15
$20 \leqslant t < 40$	5

Bhavna made some mistakes when she drew a histogram for this information.

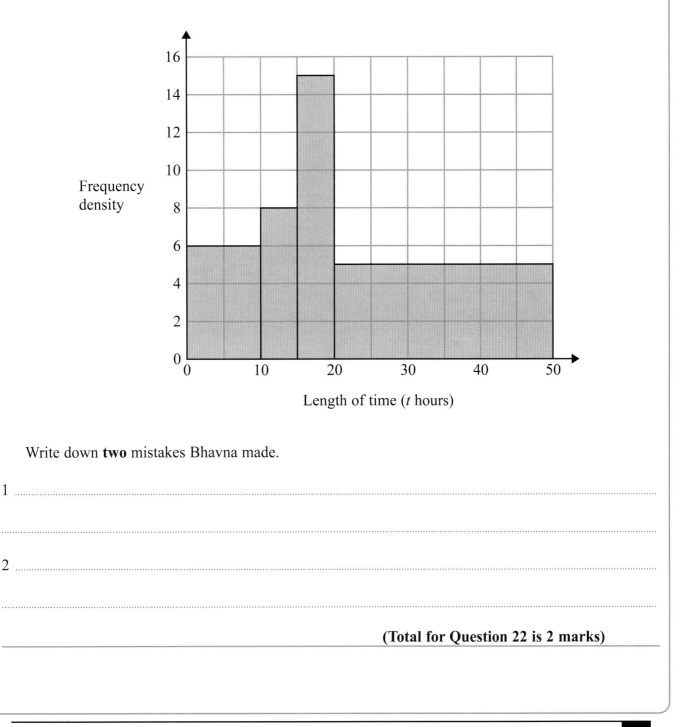

Length of time (*t* hours)

Write down **two** mistakes Bhavna made.

1 ....

....

2 ....

....

(Total for Question 22 is 2 marks)

23 Show that $\dfrac{1}{1+\dfrac{1}{\sqrt{2}}}$ can be written as $2 - \sqrt{2}$

(Total for Question 23 is 3 marks)

24 John has an empty box.

He puts some red counters and some blue counters into the box.

The ratio of the number of red counters to the number of blue counters is 1 : 4

Linda takes at random 2 counters from the box.

The probability that she takes 2 red counters is $\dfrac{6}{155}$

How many red counters did John put into the box?

(Total for Question 24 is 4 marks)

© Pearson Education Limited 2015

25 $A(-2, 1)$, $B(6, 5)$ and $C(4, k)$ are the vertices of a right-angled triangle ABC.
Angle ABC is the right angle.

Find an equation of the line that passes through A and C.
Give your answer in the form $ay + bx = c$ where a, b and c are integers.

....

(Total for Question 25 is 5 marks)

TOTAL FOR PAPER IS 80 MARKS

Pearson Edexcel Level 1/Level 2 GCSE (9-1) in Mathematics - Sample Assessment Materials (SAMs) - Issue 2 - June 2015
© Pearson Education Limited 2015

Paper 1MA1: 1H

Question	Working	Answer		Notes
1		32.968	M1	for correct method (condone one error)
			A1	for digits 32968
			A1	ft (dep M1) for correct placement of decimal pt
2		$m^2 + 10m + 21$	M1	for at least 3 terms out of a maximum of 4 correct from expansion
			A1	
3		152	M1	Start to method $ABD = 38^o$ **and** BAD or DBC or $DCB = 38^o$
			M1	ADB or $BDC = 180 - 2 \times 38$ ($=104$)
			A1	for 152 with working
4 (a)		48	P1	start to process eg. 3×80 ($=240$)
			P1	'240' $\div$ 5
			A1	
(b)			C1	eg. she may drive a different distance and therefore her average speed could be different

Question	Working	Answer	Notes	
5		28	P1	Process to start to solve problem eg. $\dfrac{3}{5} \times 40$ **or** divide any number in the ratio 3:2
			P1	Second step in process to solve problem eg. $\dfrac{2}{5} \times 10$ or find number of males/females under 25 for candidate's chosen number
			P1	for complete process
			A1	
6		Correct sketch	C1	interprets diagram eg. draw a solid shape with at least two correct dimensions
			C1	draws correct prism with all necessary dimensions.
7		400	P1	Start to process eg. $1200 \div 60$
			A1	400 oe (accept number of whole pizzas eg. $400 \div 4 = 100$ with 4 people per pizza)
			C1	Eg. Assumption that sample is representative of population – it may not be all 1200 people are going to the party – need less pizza if they don't, assume 4 people per pizza – if different may need more/fewer pizzas

Paper 1MA1: 1H

Question	Working	Answer		Notes
8		$x = 21$, $y = 50$	P1	process to start solving problem eg. form an appropriate equation
			P1	complete process to isolate terms in x
			A1	for $x = 21$
			P1	complete process to find second variable
			A1	$y = 50$
9		2.7×10^4	M1	For evidence of a correct method eg. $27 \times 10^{-4+7}$
			A1	
10 (a)		8	B1	
(b)		$\dfrac{25}{4}$ oe	M1	for correct first step
			A1	
11 (a)		2.5×10^{24}	P1	process to estimate or divide
			P1	a complete process eg. $(1 \times 10^3) \div (4 \times 10^{-22})$
			A1	
(b)		Under-estimate	C1	ft from (i) Eg. under estimate as number rounded up but in denominator of fraction

Paper 1MA1: 1H

Question		Working	Answer		Notes
12			150 000	M1	$60 \div 100^2$ **or** $900 \div 60$ **or** $900 \div$ "60"
				A1	
13			6.4	P1	Start to process eg. find scale factor (0.4) or $\dfrac{AE}{4} = \dfrac{4}{10}$
				P1	Complete process to find area
				A1	
14	(a)	Median = 22; lq = 18; uq = 26	Box plot	C1	Start to interpret information eg. one of median, lq, uq correct
				C1	Starts to communicate information eg. box plot with box, whiskers and at least 3 of median, lq, uq, min and max correct
				C1	Correct box plot
	(b)		Ben with reason	M1	interpret information eg ft from box plot to find iqr (8) or range (11)
				C1	ft eg. Ben with lower iqr (8) and range (11)
15			No with reason	C1	Starts to formulate reason eg. No with partial explanation or 0.8×0.7 or starts to use figures
				C1	No with full explanation eg. $0.8 \times 0.7 = 0.56$ so only 44% reduction
16			$5(2x + 1)(2x - 1)$	M1	for $5(4x^2 - 1)$
				A1	

 Pearson Edexcel Level 1/Level 2 GCSE (9-1) in Mathematics - Sample Assessment Materials (SAMs) - Issue 2 - June 2015
© Pearson Education Limited 2015

Paper 1MA1: 1H

Question	Working	Answer		Notes
17		$a = \dfrac{7 - 3r}{r - 2}$	M1	Remove fraction and expand brackets
			M1	Isolate terms in a
			A1	
18		Given result	M1	For length scale factor eg $\sqrt{\dfrac{4}{9}}$ **or** 120 : 405
			M1	$\left(\sqrt{\dfrac{4}{9}}\right)^{3} \times 405$ **or** $2^3 : 3^3$ (from 120 : 405)
			A1	120 from correct arithmetic **or** conclusion relating $2^3 : 3^3$ with $2^2 : 3^2$ with correct working
19		$x > 4$, $x < -1$	M1	rearrange quadratic and factorise
			M1	critical values of 4 and -1 found
			A1	
20 (a)		$(-2, -2)(-6, -2)$ $(-2,-4)(-4, -4)$	M1	Shape drawn in correct orientation
			A1	
(b)		Enlargement sf -0.5 centre (0,0)	C1	

Question	Working	Answer		Notes
21 (a)		25	C1	For interpretation eg.. area equated to 1750m
			P1	Process to solve equation
			A1	
(b)		Description	C1	Start to interpret graph eg. describe or give acceleration for one stage of the journey or state that acceleration is constant in all 3 parts
			C1	Describe acceleration for all stages of the journey or give acceleration for all 3 stages (1.25 m/s^2 ; 0 m/s^2 ; -0.625 m/s^2)
22			C1	C1 for frequencies used for heights or areas not proportional to frequencies
			C1	C1 for 2nd mistake - final bar of wrong width
23		Given result	C1	Correct first step towards simplifying expression eg. $\dfrac{\sqrt{2}}{\sqrt{2}+1}$
			C1	Correct step to rationalise denominator
			C1	Conclusion to given result

Pearson Edexcel Level 1/Level 2 GCSE (9-1) in Mathematics - Sample Assessment Materials (SAMs) - Issue 2 - June 2015
© Pearson Education Limited 2015

Question	Working	Answer		Notes
24		25	P1	For process to start to solve. Eg use of x and $4x$ or $x/5x$ and $4x/5x$
			P1	process to form equation eg $\dfrac{x}{5x} \times \dfrac{x-1}{5x-1} = \dfrac{6}{155}$
			P1	Processes to eliminate fractions and reduce equation to linear form eg. $155x - 155 = 150x - 30$
			A1	
25		$3y - 4x = 11$	P1	process to start to solve problem eg. draw a diagram, find gradient of AB (0.5)
			P1	process to use gradients eg. find gradient of BC (−2)
			P1	Process to find y coordinate of C (9)
			P1	Process to find equation of AC
			A1	

Pearson Edexcel Level 1/Level 2 GCSE (9-1) in Mathematics - Sample Assessment Materials (SAMs) - Issue 2 - June 2015
© Pearson Education Limited 2015

Write your name here

Surname

Other names

Pearson Edexcel
Level 1/Level 2 GCSE (9 - 1)

Centre Number

Candidate Number

Mathematics

Paper 2 (Calculator)

Higher Tier

Sample Assessment Materials – Issue 2
Time: 1 hour 30 minutes

Paper Reference
1MA1/2H

Total Marks

You must have: Ruler graduated in centimetres and millimetres, protractor, pair of compasses, pen, HB pencil, eraser, calculator.

Instructions

- Use **black** ink or ball-point pen.
- **Fill in the boxes** at the top of this page with your name, centre number and candidate number.
- Answer **all** questions.
- Answer the questions in the spaces provided
  – *there may be more space than you need.*
- **Calculators may be used.**
- If your calculator does not have a π button, take the value of π to be 3.142 unless the question instructs otherwise.
- Diagrams are **NOT** accurately drawn, unless otherwise indicated.
- You must **show all your working out**.

Information

- The total mark for this paper is 80
- The marks for **each** question are shown in brackets
  – *use this as a guide as to how much time to spend on each question.*

Advice

- Read each question carefully before you start to answer it.
- Keep an eye on the time.
- Try to answer every question.
- Check your answers if you have time at the end.

Turn over ▶

S48574A
©2015 Pearson Education Ltd.
6/4/7/7/7/4/6/6/6/

Answer ALL questions.

Write your answers in the spaces provided.

You must write down all the stages in your working.

1   Frank, Mary and Seth shared some sweets in the ratio 4 : 5 : 7
    Seth got 18 more sweets than Frank.

    Work out the total number of sweets they shared.

....

(Total for Question 1 is 3 marks)

2   *PQR* is a right-angled triangle.

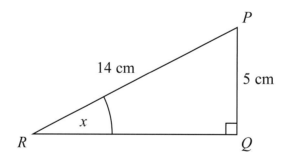

    Work out the size of the angle marked *x*.
    Give your answer correct to 1 decimal place.

.... °

(Total for Question 2 is 2 marks)

3 Here are the first four terms of an arithmetic sequence.

    6   10   14   18

(a) Write an expression, in terms of n, for the nth term of this sequence.

....

(2)

The nth term of a different arithmetic sequence is $3n + 5$

(b) Is 108 a term of this sequence?
Show how you get your answer.

(2)

(Total for Question 3 is 4 marks)

4 Axel and Lethna are driving along a motorway.

They see a road sign.
The road sign shows the distance to Junction 8
It also shows the average time drivers take to get to Junction 8

> To Junction 8
> 30 miles
> 26 minutes

The speed limit on the motorway is 70 mph.

Lethna says

"We will have to drive faster than the speed limit to drive 30 miles in 26 minutes."

Is Lethna right?
You must show how you get your answer.

(Total for Question 4 is 3 marks)

 Pearson Edexcel Level 1/Level 2 GCSE (9-1) in Mathematics - Sample Assessment Materials (SAMs) - Issue 2 - June 2015
© Pearson Education Limited 2015

5 The table shows some information about the foot lengths of 40 adults.

Foot length (f cm)	Number of adults
$16 \leqslant f < 18$	3
$18 \leqslant f < 20$	6
$20 \leqslant f < 22$	10
$22 \leqslant f < 24$	12
$24 \leqslant f < 26$	9

(a) Write down the modal class interval.

....

(1)

(b) Calculate an estimate for the mean foot length.

.... cm

(3)

(Total for Question 5 is 4 marks)

6 Triangles *ABD* and *BCD* are right-angled triangles.

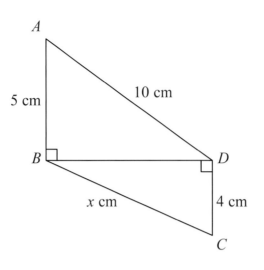

Work out the value of *x*.
Give your answer correct to 2 decimal places.

....

(Total for Question 6 is 4 marks)

7 The graph of $y = f(x)$ is drawn on the grid.

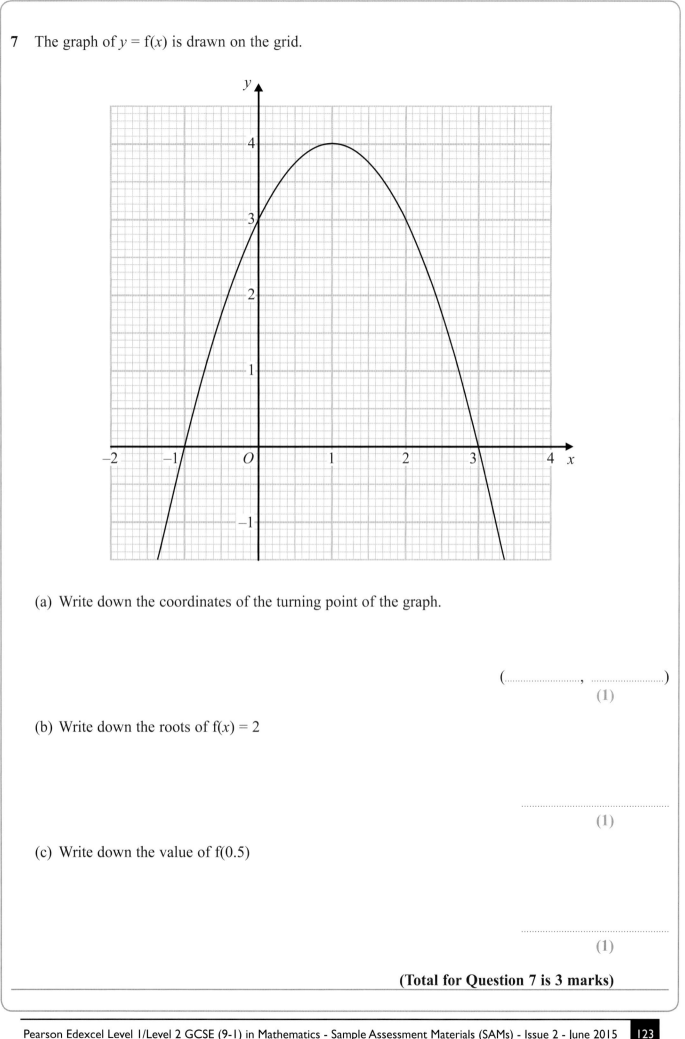

(a) Write down the coordinates of the turning point of the graph.

(........................, ...)

(1)

(b) Write down the roots of $f(x) = 2$

....

(1)

(c) Write down the value of $f(0.5)$

....

(1)

(Total for Question 7 is 3 marks)

8 In a box of pens, there are

three times as many red pens as green pens
and two times as many green pens as blue pens.

For the pens in the box, write down
the ratio of the number of red pens to the number of green pens to the number of blue pens.

....

(Total for Question 8 is 2 marks)

9   *ABCD* is a rectangle.
   EFGH is a trapezium.

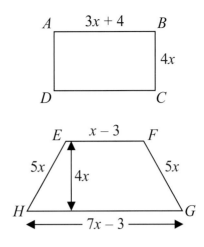

All measurements are in centimetres.
The perimeters of these two shapes are the same.

Work out the area of the rectangle.

.... cm²

(Total for Question 9 is 5 marks)

10 Katy invests £2000 in a savings account for 3 years.

The account pays compound interest at an annual rate of

$\qquad$ 2.5% for the first year

$\qquad$ $x\%$ for the second year

$\qquad$ $x\%$ for the third year

There is a total amount of £2124.46 in the savings account at the end of 3 years.

(a) Work out the rate of interest in the second year.

....

(4)

Katy goes to work by train.

The cost of her weekly train ticket increases by 12.5% to £225

(b) Work out the cost of her weekly train ticket before this increase.

£...

(2)

(Total for Question 10 is 6 marks)

11

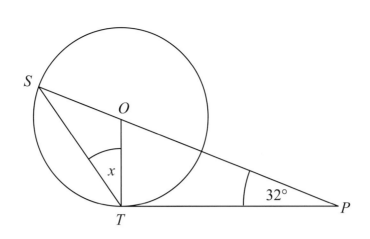

S and T are points on the circumference of a circle, centre O.
PT is a tangent to the circle.
SOP is a straight line.
Angle OPT = 32°

Work out the size of the angle marked x.
You must give a reason for each stage of your working.

(Total for Question 11 is 4 marks)

12 A and B are two sets of traffic lights on a road.

The probability that a car is stopped by lights A is 0.4

If a car is stopped by lights A, then the probability that the car is **not** stopped by lights B is 0.7

If a car is **not** stopped by lights A, then the probability that the car is **not** stopped by lights B is 0.2

(a) Complete the probability tree diagram for this information.

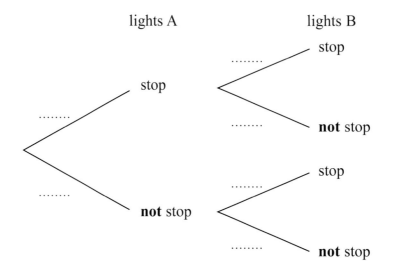

lights A   lights B

(2)

Mark drove along this road.
He was stopped by just one of the sets of traffic lights.

(b) Is it more likely that he was stopped by lights A or by lights B?
You must show your working.

(3)

(Total for Question 12 is 5 marks)

13 d is inversely proportional to c

When $c = 280$, $d = 25$

Find the value of d when $c = 350$

$d =$ ....

(Total for Question 13 is 3 marks)

14 Prove algebraically that

$(2n + 1)^2 - (2n + 1)$ is an even number

for all positive integer values of n.

(Total for Question 14 is 3 marks)

15 Prove algebraically that the recurring decimal $0.2\dot{5}$ has the value $\dfrac{23}{90}$

(Total for Question 15 is 2 marks)

16 Show that $\dfrac{1}{6x^2 + 7x - 5} \div \dfrac{1}{4x^2 - 1}$ simplifies to $\dfrac{ax + b}{cx + d}$ where a, b, c and d are integers.

(Total for Question 16 is 3 marks)

17 The diagram shows a sector of a circle of radius 7 cm.

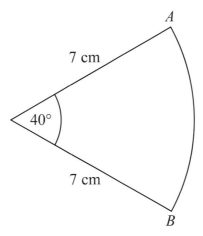

Work out the length of arc *AB*.
Give your answer correct to 3 significant figures.

.... cm

(Total for Question 17 is 2 marks)

18 $m = \dfrac{\sqrt{s}}{t}$ $s = 3.47$ correct to 3 significant figures

                            $t = 8.132$ correct to 4 significant figures

By considering bounds, work out the value of m to a suitable degree of accuracy.
Give a reason for your answer.

(Total for Question 18 is 5 marks)

18 $m = \dfrac{\sqrt{s}}{t}$ $s = 3.47$ correct to 3 significant figures

19 The graph of $y = f(x)$ is shown on both grids below.

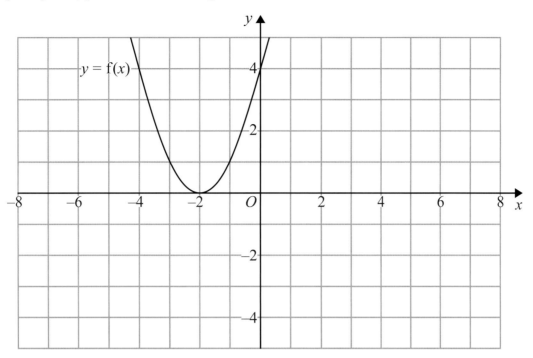

(a) On the grid above, sketch the graph of $y = f(-x)$

(1)

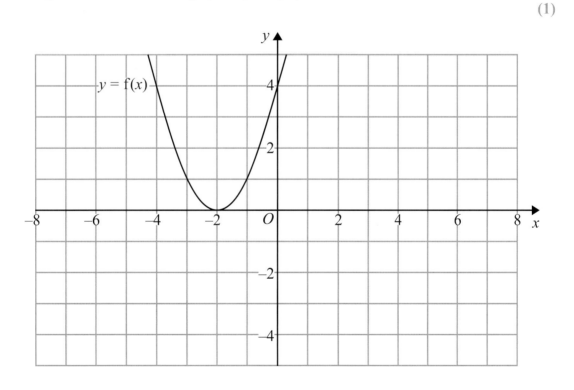

(b) On this grid, sketch the graph of $y = -f(x) + 3$

(1)

(Total for Question 19 is 2 marks)

© Pearson Education Limited 2015

20 Solve algebraically the simultaneous equations

$$x^2 + y^2 = 25$$
$$y - 2x = 5$$

(Total for Question 20 is 5 marks)

21 In triangle *RPQ*,

$RP = 8.7$ cm
$PQ = 5.2$ cm
Angle *PRQ* = 32°

(a) Assuming that angle *PQR* is an acute angle,
   calculate the area of triangle *RPQ*.
   Give your answer correct to 3 significant figures.

....cm²

(4)

(b) If you did not know that angle *PQR* is an acute angle, what effect would this have on
   your calculation of the area of triangle *RPQ*?

....

....

....

(1)

(Total for Question 21 is 5 marks)

22 A frustum is made by removing a small cone from a large cone as shown in the diagram.

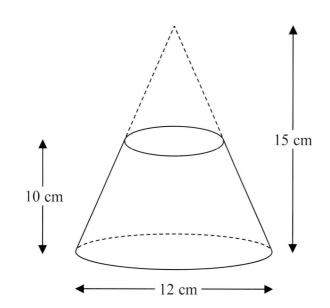

15 cm

10 cm

12 cm

Volume of cone $= \dfrac{1}{3}\pi r^2 h$

h

r

The frustum is made from glass.
The glass has a density of 2.5 g / cm³

Work out the mass of the frustum.
Give your answer to an appropriate degree of accuracy.

.... g

(Total for Question 22 is 5 marks)

TOTAL FOR PAPER IS 80 MARKS

© Pearson Education Limited 2015

Paper 1MA1: 2H

Question	Working	Answer		Notes
1		96	P1	a strategy to start to solve the problem eg $18 \div (7 - 4)$ (=6)
			P1	for completing the process of solution eg "6" $\times (4 + 5 + 7)$
			A1	cao
2		20.9	M1	correct recall of appropriate formula eg $\sin x = \dfrac{5}{14}$
			A1	for 20.9(248…)
3 (a)		$4n+2$	M1	start to deduce nth term from information given eg $4n+k$ where $k \neq 2$
			A1	cao
(b)		No (supported)	M1	starts method that could lead to a deduction eg uses inverse operations
			C1	for a convincing argument eg 34 is 107 so NO; $(108-5) \div 3$ is not an integer
4		conclusion	P1	$30 \div 70$ (=0.428) | $26 \div 60$ (=0.4333…) | $30 \div 26$ (=1.153…)
		(supported)	P1	$60 \times$ "0.428…" | $70 \times$"0.4333…" | $60 \times$ "1.153…"
			C1	for conclusion linked to 25.7 mins, 30.3 miles or 69.2 mph

© Pearson Education Limited 2015

Paper 1MA1: 2H

Question		Working	Answer		Notes
5	(a)		$22 \leq f < 24$	B1	
	(b)		21.9	M1	$x \times f$ using midpoints
				M1	(dep on previous mark) "$x \times f$" ÷ 40
				A1	accept 22 if working seen
6			9.54	P1	$10^2 - 5^2 (=75)$
				P1	"75" $+ 4^2 (=91)$
				P1	$\sqrt{(10^2 - 5^2 + 4^2)}$
				A1	$9.53 - 9.54$
7	(a)		(1, 4)	B1	
	(b)		−0.4, 2.4	B1	
	(c)		3.75	B1	accept 3.7 − 3.8
8			6 : 2 : 1	M1	for correct interpretation of any one statement eg. 3 : 1; 1 : 0.5
				A1	accept any equivalent ratio eg. 3 : 1 : 0.5

Pearson Edexcel Level 1/Level 2 GCSE (9-1) in Mathematics - Sample Assessment Materials (SAMs) - Issue 2 - June 2015
© Pearson Education Limited 2015

Question	Working	Answer	Notes	
9		203	P1	translate into algebra for rectangle: $4x+4x+3x+4+3x+4$ $(=14x+8)$ or for trapezium: $5x+5x+x-3+7x-3$ $(=18x-6)$
			P1	equating: eg $18x-6=14x+8$ $(4x=14)$
			A1	solving for x: $x=14/4 = 3.5$ oe
			P1	process to find area: "3.5" × 3+4 (ft) or "3.5" × 4 ft
			A1	cao
10 (a)		1.8%	P1	for start to process eg. 2000×1.025 $(=2050)$
			P1	for process to use all given information eg "2050" $\times m^2 = 2124.46$ or "2050" $\times \left(1+\dfrac{x}{100}\right)^2 = 2124.46$
			P1	for process to find their unknown eg $m = \sqrt{\dfrac{2124.46}{2050}}$ $(= 1.01799....)$
			A1	for 1.79% − 1.8 %
(b)		200	M1	$225 \div 1.125$ oe
			A1	

Paper 1MA1: 2H

Question		Working	Answer		Notes
11			29°	C1	angle $OTP = 90°$, quoted or shown on the diagram
				M1	method that leads to 180 – (90 + 32) or 58 shown at *TOP* OR that leads to 122 shown at *SOT*
				M1	complete method leading to "58"÷2 or (180 – "122") ÷ 2 or 29 shown at *TSP*
				C1	for angle of 29° clearly indicated and appropriate reasons linked to method eg angle between radius and tangent = 90° and sum of angles in a triangle = 180°; ext angle of a triangle equal to sum of int opp angles and base angles of an isos triangle are equal or angle at centre = 2x angle at circumference or ext angle of a triangle equal to sum of int opp angles
12	(a)		0.4, 0.6	B1	correctly placing probs for light A eg 0.4, 0.6
			0.3, 0.7, 0.8, 0.2	B1	correctly placing probs for light B eg 0.3, 0.7, 0.8, 0.2
	(b)		B with correct probabilities	P1	(ft) eg 0.4 × 0.3 or 0.6 × 0.8 or 1–(0.28+0.12)
				P1	both sets of correct probability calculations
				C1	Correct interpretation of results with correct comparable results
13			20	M1	Establishing method linked to proportion eg $d=k÷c$ or $25=k÷280$
				M1	(dep) substitution eg $d = 7000 ÷ 350$ or $25 × 280 ÷ 350$ oe
				A1	cao

© Pearson Education Limited 2015

Paper 1MA1: 2H

Question	Working	Answer		Notes
14	$(4n^2+2n+2n+1)$ $-(2n+1)=$ $4n^2+4n+1-2n-1$ $=4n^2+2n$ $=2n(2n+1)$	proof (supported)	M1	for 3 out of 4 terms correct in the expansion of $(2n+1)^2$ **or** $(2n+1)\{(2n+1)-1\}$
			P1	for $4n^2+2n$ or equivalent expression in factorised form
			C1	for convincing statement using $2n(2n+1)$ or $2(2n^2+n)$ or $4n^2+2n$ to prove the result
15		$\dfrac{23}{90}$	M1	For a fully complete method as far as finding two correct decimals that, when subtracted, give a terminating decimal (or integer) and showing intention to subtract eg $x=0.2\dot{5}$ so $10x=2.5\dot{5}$ then $9x=2.3$ leading to…
			A1	correct working to conclusion
16		$\dfrac{2x+1}{3x+5}$	M1	for $(3x\pm5)(2x\pm1)$ or $(2x+1)(2x-1)$
			M1	$\dfrac{1}{(3x\pm5)(2x\pm1)}\times(2x+1)(2x-1)$
			A1	
17		4.89	M1	$\dfrac{40}{360}\times2\times\pi\times7$ oe
			A1	$4.8-4.9$

© Pearson Education Limited 2015

Paper 1MA1: 2H

Question	Working	Answer		Notes
18		0.229 With Explanation	B1	Finding bound of s: 3.465 or 3.475 or 3.474999… or Finding bound of t: 8.1315 or 8.1325 or 8.132499…
			P1	Use of "upper bound" and "lower bound" in equation
			P1	Process of choosing correct bounds eg $\dfrac{\sqrt{3.475}}{8.1315}$ or $\dfrac{\sqrt{3.465}}{8.1325}$
			A1	For 0.2292… and 0.2288.. from correct working
			C1	For 0.229 from 0.2292.. and 0.2288.. since both LB and UB round to 0.229
19 (a)		Sketch	P1	Parabola passes through all three of the points (0, 4), (2,0), (4, 4)
(b)		Sketch	P1	Parabola passes through all three of the points $(-4, -1)$, $(-2,2)$, $(0, -1)$
20		$x=0, y=5$ $x=-4, y=-3$	M1	Initial process of substitution eg $x^2 + (2x + 5)^2$ (=25)
			M1	for expanding and simplifying eg $x^2 + 4x^2 +10x +10x +25$ (=25)
			M1	Use of factorisation or correct substitution into quadratic formula or completing the square to solve an equation of the form $ax^2 + bx + c = 0, a \neq 0$
			A1	correct values of x or y
			C1	$x = 0, x = -4, y = 5, y = -3$ correctly matched x and y values

© Pearson Education Limited 2015

Question	Working	Answer	Notes
21 (a)		130	P1 start to process eg draw a labelled triangle or use of sine rule $\dfrac{\sin Q}{8.7} = \dfrac{\sin 32}{5.2}$
			P1 process to find of Q eg $Q = \sin^{-1}\left[\dfrac{\sin 32}{5.2} \times 8.7\right]$
			P1 process to find area of triangle PRQ.
			A1 22.5 − 22.6
(b)			C1 angle PRQ is obtuse so need to find area of two triangles.
22		1361	P1 process using similar triangles to find base of small cone eg. 4 cm used as diameter or 2 cm used as radius
			P1 process to find volume of one cone
			P1 complete process to find volume of frustum
			P1 complete process to find mass or 1360 − 1362
			A1 1361 or 1360 or 1400

Pearson Edexcel Level 1/Level 2 GCSE (9-1) in Mathematics - Sample Assessment Materials (SAMs) - Issue 2 - June 2015
© Pearson Education Limited 2015

Write your name here

Surname	Other names

Pearson Edexcel
Level 1/Level 2 GCSE (9 - 1)

Centre Number

Candidate Number

Mathematics

Paper 3 (Calculator)

Higher Tier

Sample Assessment Materials – Issue 2
Time: 1 hour 30 minutes

Paper Reference
1MA1/3H

Total Marks

You must have: Ruler graduated in centimetres and millimetres, protractor, pair of compasses, pen, HB pencil, eraser, calculator.

Instructions

- Use **black** ink or ball-point pen.
- **Fill in the boxes** at the top of this page with your name, centre number and candidate number.
- Answer **all** questions.
- Answer the questions in the spaces provided
  – *there may be more space than you need.*
- **Calculators may be used.**
- If your calculator does not have a π button, take the value of π to be 3.142 unless the question instructs otherwise.
- Diagrams are **NOT** accurately drawn, unless otherwise indicated.
- You must **show all your working out**.

Information

- The total mark for this paper is 80
- The marks for **each** question are shown in brackets
  – *use this as a guide as to how much time to spend on each question.*

Advice

- Read each question carefully before you start to answer it.
- Keep an eye on the time.
- Try to answer every question.
- Check your answers if you have time at the end.

Turn over ▶

Answer ALL questions.

Write your answers in the spaces provided.

You must write down all the stages in your working.

1   The diagram shows a trapezium *ABCD* and two identical semicircles.

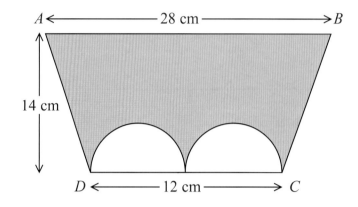

The centre of each semicircle is on *DC*.

Work out the area of the shaded region.
Give your answer correct to 3 significant figures.

.... cm²

(Total for Question 1 is 4 marks)

2 Asif is going on holiday to Turkey.

The exchange rate is £1 = 3.5601 lira.

Asif changes £550 to lira.

(a) Work out how many lira he should get.
   Give your answer to the nearest lira.

.... lira

(2)

Asif sees a pair of shoes in Turkey.
The shoes cost 210 lira.

Asif does not have a calculator.
He uses £2 = 7 lira to work out the approximate cost of the shoes in pounds.

(b) Use £2 = 7 lira to show that the approximate cost of the shoes is £60

(2)

(c) Is using £2 = 7 lira instead of using £1 = 3.5601 lira a sensible start to Asif's method
   to work out the cost of the shoes in pounds?

   You must give a reason for your answer.

....

....

(1)

(Total for Question 2 is 5 marks)

3   Here are the first six terms of a Fibonacci sequence.

$$1 \quad 1 \quad 2 \quad 3 \quad 5 \quad 8$$

The rule to continue a Fibonacci sequence is,

the next term in the sequence is the sum of the two previous terms.

(a) Find the 9th term of this sequence.

....
(1)

The first three terms of a different Fibonacci sequence are

$$a \quad b \quad a + b$$

(b) Show that the 6th term of this sequence is $3a + 5b$

(2)

Given that the 3rd term is 7 and the 6th term is 29,

(c) find the value of a and the value of b.

....
(3)

(Total for Question 3 is 6 marks)

 Pearson Edexcel Level 1/Level 2 GCSE (9-1) in Mathematics - Sample Assessment Materials (SAMs) - Issue 2 - June 2015
© Pearson Education Limited 2015

4   In a survey, the outside temperature and the number of units of electricity used for heating were recorded for ten homes.

The scatter diagram shows this information.

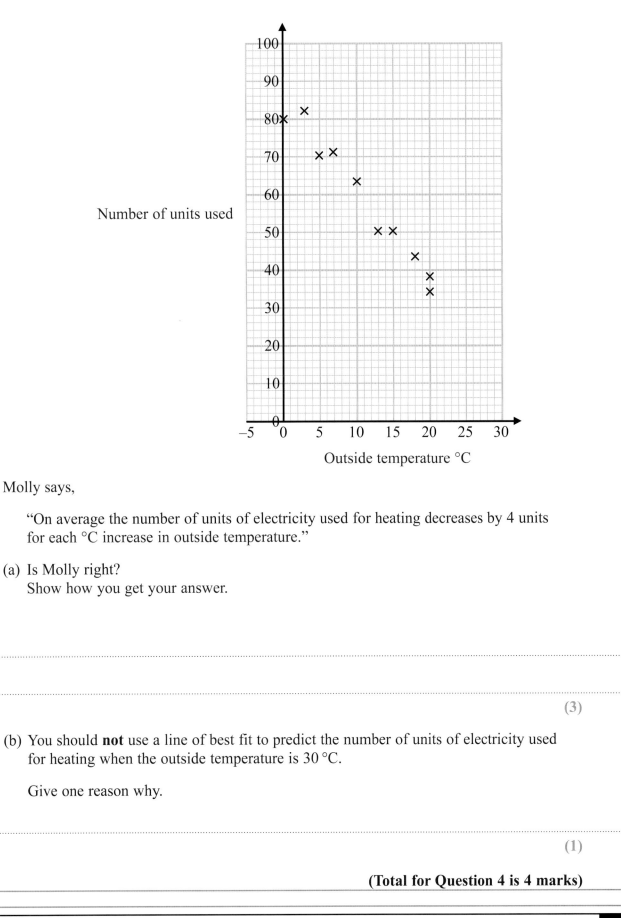

Molly says,

"On average the number of units of electricity used for heating decreases by 4 units for each °C increase in outside temperature."

(a) Is Molly right?
    Show how you get your answer.

....

....

(3)

(b) You should **not** use a line of best fit to predict the number of units of electricity used for heating when the outside temperature is 30 °C.

Give one reason why.

....

(1)

(Total for Question 4 is 4 marks)

5 Henry is thinking of having a water meter.

These are the two ways he can pay for the water he uses.

Water Meter

A charge of £28.20 per year

plus

91.22p for every cubic metre of water used

1 cubic metre = 1000 litres

No Water Meter

A charge of £107 per year

Henry uses an average of 180 litres of water each day.

Use this information to determine whether or not Henry should have a water meter.

(Total for Question 5 is 5 marks)

 Pearson Edexcel Level 1/Level 2 GCSE (9-1) in Mathematics - Sample Assessment Materials (SAMs) - Issue 2 - June 2015
© Pearson Education Limited 2015

6 Liz buys packets of coloured buttons.

There are 8 red buttons in each packet of red buttons.
There are 6 silver buttons in each packet of silver buttons.
There are 5 gold buttons in each packet of gold buttons.

Liz buys equal numbers of red buttons, silver buttons and gold buttons.

How many packets of each colour of buttons did Liz buy?

.....................................packets of red buttons

.....................................packets of silver buttons

.....................................packets of gold buttons

(Total for Question 6 is 3 marks)

7 The cumulative frequency table shows the marks some students got in a test.

Mark (*m*)	Cumulative frequency
$0 < m \leqslant 10$	8
$0 < m \leqslant 20$	23
$0 < m \leqslant 30$	48
$0 < m \leqslant 40$	65
$0 < m \leqslant 50$	74
$0 < m \leqslant 60$	80

(a) On the grid, plot a cumulative frequency graph for this information.

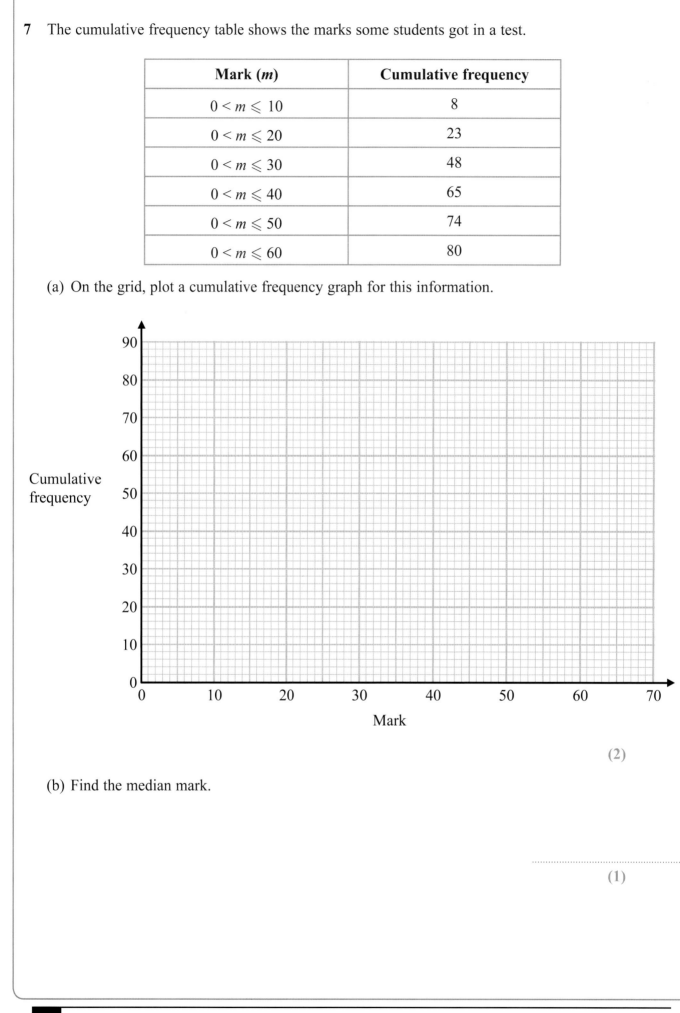

(2)

(b) Find the median mark.

....

(1)

Students either pass the test or fail the test.
The pass mark is set so that 3 times as many students fail the test as pass the test.

(c) Find an estimate for the lowest possible pass mark.

....

(3)

(Total for Question 7 is 6 marks)

8   Write 0.000068 in standard form.

....

(Total for Question 8 is 1 mark)

9 (a) Factorise $y^2 + 7y + 6$

....
(2)

(b) Solve $6x + 4 > x + 17$

....
(2)

(c) n is an integer with $-5 < 2n \leqslant 6$

Write down all the values of n

....
(2)

(Total for Question 9 is 6 marks)

10 The function f is such that

$$f(x) = 4x - 1$$

(a) Find $f^{-1}(x)$

$f^{-1}(x) =$ ....
(2)

The function g is such that

$$g(x) = kx^2 \text{ where } k \text{ is a constant.}$$

Given that $fg(2) = 12$

(b) work out the value of k

$k =$ ....
(2)

(Total for Question 10 is 4 marks)

 Pearson Edexcel Level 1/Level 2 GCSE (9-1) in Mathematics - Sample Assessment Materials (SAMs) - Issue 2 - June 2015
© Pearson Education Limited 2015

11 Solve $x^2 - 5x + 3 = 0$

Give your solutions correct to 3 significant figures.

....

(Total for Question 11 is 3 marks)

© Pearson Education Limited 2015

12 Sami asked 50 people which drinks they liked from tea, coffee and milk.

All 50 people like at least one of the drinks
19 people like all three drinks.
16 people like tea and coffee but do **not** like milk.
21 people like coffee and milk.
24 people like tea and milk.
40 people like coffee.
1 person likes only milk.

Sami selects at random one of the 50 people.

(a) Work out the probability that this person likes tea.

(4)

(b) Given that the person selected at random from the 50 people likes tea,
find the probability that this person also likes exactly one other drink.

(2)

(Total for Question 12 is 6 marks)

13 *ABCD* is a rhombus.

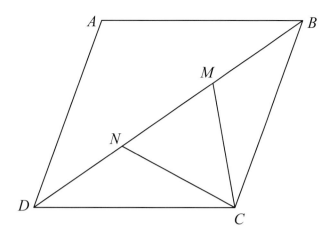

M and *N* are points on *BD* such that *DN* = *MB*.

Prove that triangle *DNC* is congruent to triangle *BMC*.

(Total for Question 13 is 3 marks)

14 (a) Show that the equation $x^3 + 4x = 1$ has a solution between $x = 0$ and $x = 1$

(2)

(b) Show that the equation $x^3 + 4x = 1$ can be arranged to give $x = \dfrac{1}{4} - \dfrac{x^3}{4}$

(1)

(c) Starting with $x_0 = 0$, use the iteration formula $x_{n+1} = \dfrac{1}{4} - \dfrac{x_n^3}{4}$ twice,

to find an estimate for the solution of $x^3 + 4x = 1$

(3)

(Total for Question 14 is 6 marks)

Pearson Edexcel Level 1/Level 2 GCSE (9-1) in Mathematics - Sample Assessment Materials (SAMs) - Issue 2 - June 2015
© Pearson Education Limited 2015

15 There are 17 men and 26 women in a choir.
The choir is going to sing at a concert.

One of the men and one of the women are going to be chosen to make a pair to sing the first song.

(a) Work out the number of different pairs that can be chosen.

....

(2)

Two of the men are to be chosen to make a pair to sing the second song.

Ben thinks the number of different pairs that can be chosen is 136
Mark thinks the number of different pairs that can be chosen is 272

(b) Who is correct, Ben or Mark?
Give a reason for your answer.

....

....

(1)

(Total for Question 15 is 3 marks)

16 *VABCD* is a solid pyramid.

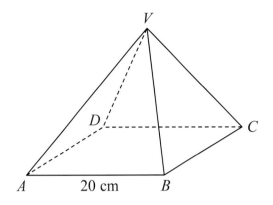

ABCD is a square of side 20 cm.

The angle between any sloping edge and the plane *ABCD* is 55°

Calculate the surface area of the pyramid.
Give your answer correct to 2 significant figures.

....cm²

(Total for Question 16 is 5 marks)

17 Louis and Robert are investigating the growth in the population of a type of bacteria. They have two flasks A and B.

At the start of day 1, there are 1000 bacteria in flask A.
The population of bacteria grows exponentially at the rate of 50% per day.

(a) Show that the population of bacteria in flask A at the start of each day forms a geometric progression.

(2)

The population of bacteria in flask A at the start of the 10th day is k times the population of bacteria in flask A at the start of the 6th day.

(b) Find the value of k.

....
(2)

At the start of day 1 there are 1000 bacteria in flask B.
The population of bacteria in flask B grows exponentially at the rate of 30% per day.

(c) Sketch a graph to compare the size of the population of bacteria in flask A and in flask B.

(1)

(Total for Question 17 is 5 marks)

18

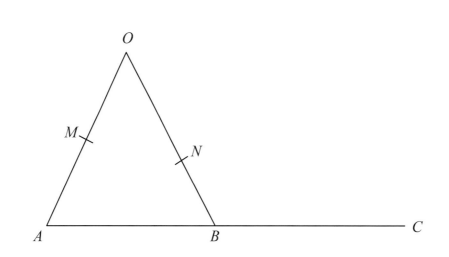

OMA, ONB and ABC are straight lines.
M is the midpoint of OA.
B is the midpoint of AC.
$\overrightarrow{OA} = 6\mathbf{a}$ $\overrightarrow{OB} = 6\mathbf{b}$ $\overrightarrow{ON} = k\mathbf{b}$ where k is a scalar quantity.

Given that MNC is a straight line, find the value of k.

BLANK PAGE

© Pearson Education Limited 2015

BLANK PAGE

© Pearson Education Limited 2015

Paper 1MA1: 3H

Question		Working	Answer		Notes
1			252	P1	For start to process eg. radius = $12 \div 4 \ (=3)$
				M1	Method to find area of trapezium or semicircle or circle
				P1	Process to find area of the shaded region
				A1	$251.7 - 252$
2	(a)	550×3.5601	1958	M1	550×3.5601
				A1	
	(b)	$210 \div 7 \times 2 = 30 \times 2$ Or $60 \div 2 = 30$ and $30 \times 7 = 210$	Shown	M1	For correct method to convert cost in UK to lira or vice versa, using Asif's approximation
				C1	Shown with correct calculations
	(c)		Correct evaluation	C1	For an evaluation e.g. It is a sensible start to the method because he can do the calculations without a calculator and 3.5 lira to the £ is a good approximation
3	(a)	8, 13, 21,	34	B1	cao
	(b)	$a, b, a + b, a + 2b, 2a + 3b$	Shown	M1	Method to show by adding pairs of successive terms $a + 2b, 2a + 3b$ shown
				C1	
	(c)	$3a + 5b = 29$ $a + b = 7$ $3a + 3b = 21$ $b = 4, a = 3$	$a = 3$ $b = 4$	P1	Process to set up two equations
				P1	Process to solve equations
				A1	

© Pearson Education Limited 2015

Paper 1MA1: 3H

Question	Working	Answer	Notes
4 (a)	Draws LOBF Finds ht÷base $= \dfrac{85-20}{0-25} = -2.6$	No + reason	M1 Interpret question eg. draw line of best fit M1 Start to test eg. gradient e.g. $\dfrac{85-20}{0-25} = -2.6$ C1 Gradient within range $\pm(2 - 3)$ and 'no'
(b)		The LOBF would have to be used outside the data	C1 Convincing explanation
5		Have a water meter (from working with correct figures)	P1 Process to find number of litres eg. $180 \div 1000$ P1 Full process to find cost per day P1 Full process to find total cost of water used per year (accept use of alternative time period for both options) P1 Full process with consistent units for total cost of water A1 Correct decision from correct figures (88.13154 or correct figure for their time period)
6		15, 20, 24	P1 Process to start to find common multiple eg. prime factor decomposition of 6 and 8 or list of at least 3 multiples of all numbers P1 process to find number of packets for at least colour **or** 120 identified A1

© Pearson Education Limited 2015

Paper 1MA1: 3H

Question	Working	Answer		Notes
7 (a)		11A	M1	For a cumulative frequency diagram with at least 5 points plotted correctly at the ends of the intervals
			C1	For correct graph with points joined by curve or straight line segments
				[SC B1 if the shape of the graph is correct and 5 points of their points are **not** at the ends but consistently within each interval **and** joined.]
(b)		26.5	B1	$25 - 28$
(c)	$80 \div 4 \times 3 = 60$ Draw line parallel to mark axis from CF $= 50$	36.5	P1	For process to find number who failed eg $80 \div 4 \times 3 = 60$
			P1	Draw line parallel to mark axis from CF $=$ ”60” and read off
			A1	For $35 - 38$
8		6.8×10^{-5}	B1	

© Pearson Education Limited 2015

Paper 1MA1: 3H

Question	Working	Answer		Notes
9 (a)		$(y+6)(y+1)$	M1	for $(y \pm 6)(y \pm 1)$
			A1	
(b)	$6x - x > 17 - 4$	2.6	M1	for method to isolate terms in x in an inequality or an equation
			A1	oe eg. $\dfrac{13}{5}$
(c)		$-2, -1, 0, 1, 2, 3$	M1	for **or** $-2.5 < n \leq 3$ **or** $-4, -2, 0, 2, 4, 6$ **or** $-4, -3, -2, -1, 0, 1, 2, 3, 4, 5, 6$
			A1	
10 (a)		$\dfrac{x+1}{4}$	M1	start to method eg. $y = 4x - 1$ or $x = \dfrac{y+1}{4}$
			A1	oe
(b)		$\dfrac{13}{16}$	P1	for start to process eg. $f(4k) = 16k - 1$ or $g(2) = \dfrac{12+1}{4}$
			A1	

 Pearson Edexcel Level 1/Level 2 GCSE (9-1) in Mathematics - Sample Assessment Materials (SAMs) - Issue 2 - June 2015
© Pearson Education Limited 2015

Paper 1MA1: 3H

Question	Working	Answer	Notes	
11	$x = \dfrac{-5 \pm \sqrt{(-5)^2 - 4 \times 1 \times 3}}{2} =$ $\dfrac{5 \pm \sqrt{13}}{2}$	4.30 or 0.697	M1	Substitute into quadratic formula - allow sign errors
			M1	Evaluate as far as $\dfrac{5 \pm \sqrt{13}}{2}$
			A1	
12 (a)	Draws correct Venn diagram	$\dfrac{44}{50}$	M1	Begin to interpret given information e.g. 3 overlapping labelled ovals with central region correct
			M1	Extend interpretation of given information e.g. 3 overlapping labelled ovals with at least 5 regions correct
			M1	Method to communicate given information e.g. 3 overlapping labelled ovals with all regions correct including outside
			A1	oe
(b)		$\dfrac{21}{44}$	P1	For correct process to identify correct regions in Venn diagram and divide by '44'
			A1	
13	$DN = MB$ (given) $\angle NDC = \angle MBC$ (base angles of isosceles triangle) $DC = BC$ (sides of a rhombus are equal) $\therefore \Delta DNC \equiv \Delta BMC$ (SAS)	Proof	C1	One correct relevant statement
			C1	All correct relevant statements
			C1	Correct conclusion with reasons

© Pearson Education Limited 2015

Question	Working	Answer	Notes
14 (a)	$F(x) = x^3 + 4x - 1$ $F(0) = -1, F(1) = 4$	Shown	M1 Method to establish at least one root in $[0,1]$ e.g $x^3 + 4x - 1$ ($=0$) and $F(0)(= -1)$, $F(1)$ ($= 4$) oe A1 Since there is a sign change there must be at least one root in $0 < x < 1$ (as F is continuous)
(b)	$4x = 1 - x^3$ Or $\dfrac{x^3}{4} + x = \dfrac{1}{4}$	Shown	C1 for at least one correct step and no incorrect ones
(c)	$x_1 = \dfrac{1}{4} - \dfrac{0}{4} = \dfrac{1}{4}$ $x_2 = \dfrac{1}{4} - \dfrac{\left(\frac{1}{4}\right)^3}{4} = \dfrac{1}{4} - \dfrac{1}{256}$	0.246(09375) Or $\dfrac{63}{256}$	B1 $x_1 = \dfrac{1}{4}$ M1 for $x_2 = \dfrac{1}{4} - \dfrac{\left(\frac{1}{4}\right)^3}{4}$ A1 for 0.246(09375) or $\dfrac{63}{256}$ oe
15 (a)	Number of men possible is 17 Number of women possible is 26 Each man can be paired with 26 different women 17×26	442	P1 Process to find number of combinations A1
(b)		Ben with reason	C1 Convincing reason e.g. correct calculation is $17 \times 16 \div 2$

Paper 1MA1: 3H

Question		Working	Answer		Notes
16		$AC^2 = 20^2 + 20^2 = 800$ $AX^2 = 10^2 + 10^2 = 200$ $\sqrt{200} \times \tan 55 = VX \quad (= 20.19...)$ $VM^2 = \sqrt{"20.19"^2 + 10^2} \quad (= 22.54...)$ $4 \times \dfrac{1}{2} \times "22.54" \times 20 + 20^2$	1300		Let X be centre of base, M be midpoint of AB
				P1	process to find AC or AX
				P1	process to find VX or VA
				P1	process to find height of sloping face or angle of sloping face.
				P1	process to find surface area of one triangular face.
				A1	For $1300 - 1302$
17	(a)	$1000, 1500, 2250, ...$	Correct Argument	M1	Method to find 1st 3 terms
				C1	Convincing reason e.g. common ratio is 1.5
	(b)	$1000 \times 1.5^9 = k \times 1000 \times 1.5^5$ $k = \dfrac{1.5^9}{1.5^5}$	5.0625	P1	Process to find the value of k
				A1	
	(c)		Correct sketches	C1	Draws both exponential curves intersecting on y axis and clearly labelled

© Pearson Education Limited 2015

Question	Working	Answer		Notes
18	$\overrightarrow{OM} = 3\mathbf{a}$ $\overrightarrow{AB} = 6\mathbf{b} - 6\mathbf{a}$ $\overrightarrow{MC} = 3\mathbf{a} + 2(6\mathbf{b} - 6\mathbf{a})$ $= 12\mathbf{b} - 9\mathbf{a}$ $= 3(4\mathbf{b} - 3\mathbf{a})$ $\overrightarrow{MN} = k\mathbf{b} - 3\mathbf{a}$ MNC is a straight line so $\overrightarrow{MC}$ is a scalar multiple of $\overrightarrow{MN}$	4	P1	For process to start e.g. $\overrightarrow{OM} = 3\mathbf{a}$ or $\overrightarrow{MA} = 3\mathbf{a}$
			P1	For process to find $\overrightarrow{AB}$ (=6$\mathbf{b}$ – 6$\mathbf{a}$)
			P1	For process to find $\overrightarrow{MC}$ (=3$\mathbf{a}$ + 2(6$\mathbf{b}$ – 6$\mathbf{a}$) and $\overrightarrow{MN}$ (= $k\mathbf{b}$ –3$\mathbf{a}$)
			P1	For correct process to find k e.g. $3k\mathbf{b} - 9\mathbf{a} = 12\mathbf{b} - 9\mathbf{a}$
			A1	

Pearson Edexcel Level 1/Level 2 GCSE (9-1) in Mathematics - Sample Assessment Materials (SAMs) - Issue 2 - June 2015 © Pearson Education Limited 2015

7

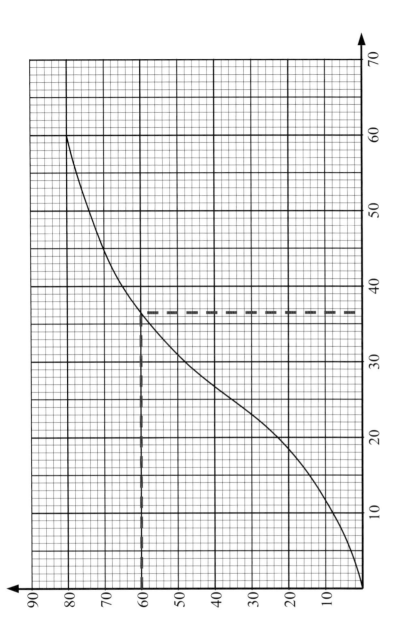

© Pearson Education Limited 2015

13

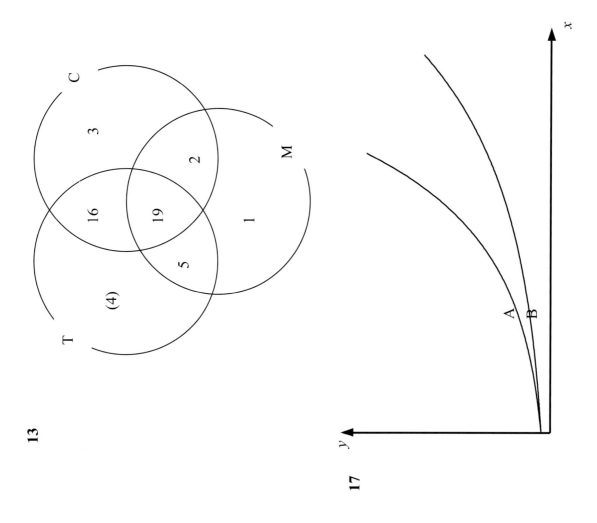

17

© Pearson Education Limited 2015

Pearson Edexcel Level 1/Level 2 GCSE (9-1) in Mathematics - Sample Assessment Materials (SAMs) - Issue 2 - June 2015
© Pearson Education Limited 2015